THE TIMES TOP 100 GRADUATE EMPLOYERS

The definitive guide to the leading employers recruiting graduates during 2024-2025.

HIGH FLIERS

HIGH FLIERS PUBLICATIONS LTD
IN ASSOCIATION WITH THE TIMES

Published by High Fliers Publications Limited
The Gridiron Building, 1 Pancras Square, London, N1C 4AG
Telephone: 020 7428 9100 *Web:* www.Top100GraduateEmployers.com

Editor Martin Birchall
Publisher Gill Thomas
Production Manager Darcy Mackay
Marketing & Social Media Ellie Goodman
Portrait Photography Phil Ripley cityspacecreative.co.uk

The Times Top 100 Graduate Employers is based on research results from *The UK Graduate Careers Survey 2024*, produced by High Fliers Research Ltd.

The greatest care has been taken in compiling this book. However, no responsibility can be accepted by the publishers or compilers for the accuracy of the information presented.

Where opinion is expressed it is that of the author or advertiser and does not necessarily coincide with the editorial views of High Fliers Publications Limited or *The Times* newspaper.

Printed and bound in Italy by L.E.G.O. S.p.A.

A CIP catalogue record for this book is available from the British Library.
ISBN 978-1-9160401-5-1

Contents

THE TIMES
TOP 100
GRADUATE EMPLOYERS

Foreword

By **Martin Birchall**
Editor, *The Times Top 100 Graduate Employers*

Welcome to the twenty-sixth edition of *The Times Top 100 Graduate Employers*, your annual guide to the UK's most prestigious and sought-after graduate employers.

When Sir Kier Starmer swept into power in this summer's General Election, he become the UK's fifth Prime Minister in five years. As well as promising a new period of stability in British politics, he and his new Chancellor, Rachel Reeves, pledged that boosting the country's economic growth would be at the heart of the Government's priorities.

This renewed focus on growth, if it is successful, should be good news for graduate employment and the wider job market in the medium-term. But it's unlikely to make a significant difference to students who are due to graduate from university in 2025.

Having bounced-back convincingly from the Coronavirus pandemic, growth in the graduate job market stalled in 2023 and there are few signs that it is likely to improve in the year ahead.

Since its first edition in 1999, *The Times Top 100 Graduate Employers* has tracked university students' success in the graduate job market. Our latest research with new graduates from the 'Class of 2024' reveals that they worked harder than any of the previous cohorts of university-leavers to secure their first graduate job.

"Few of the country's top employers recruit graduates based on their academic record – or the content of their university degree."

Half began researching their career options in their first year, almost as soon as they arrived at university – and two-fifths completed an internship or work placement with a graduate employer at the end of their second year.

By their final year, a record number of students took part in university careers fairs, employers' on-campus recruitment presentations, skills workshops, and other careers promotions during their search for a graduate job.

And when it came to applying for jobs, those graduating in the summer of 2024 applied earlier than usual to employers they were interested in, and completed an unprecedented number of applications – averaging sixteen applications per graduate, a quarter more than the previous year.

Despite all of this preparation and engagement with employers, the number of graduates from the 'Class of 2024' who received a definite job offer before leaving university actually dropped by ten per cent, compared with 2023. This means the proportion of new graduates who achieved a job offer was the second-lowest of the past decade – only the 2021 pandemic year led to a lower rate of graduate job offers.

This is a timely reminder of just how much competition there is currently for graduate-level opportunities. Employers featured in *The Times*

Top 100 Graduate Employers usually receive 40 or 50 applications per graduate vacancy – and some of the most sought-after graduate programmes can attract two or three times this number.

The experience of the 'Class of 2024' shows that students who are most-likely to be successful in the post-university job market are those who start thinking about potential future careers early and spend their time at university developing the key skills and experience that graduate employers are looking for.

Few, if any, of the country's top employers recruit graduates based on their academic record – or the content of their university degree. Many have removed school and university results from their applications altogether and are instead relying on their own battery of aptitude and psychometric tests and recorded AI-assessed interviews to determine applicants' abilities and suitability for their graduate roles.

This shift away from academic achievement to demonstrating the broad range of skills – from teamwork and leadership, to problem solving, critical thinking and resilience – that employers demand for their graduate programmes can be a difficult one to navigate.

The editorial features in this edition of *The Times Top 100 Graduate Employers* explain how your university careers service can help you prepare for employers' selection processes and achieve a successful outcome. There are tips, advice and personal guidance from several of the country's most experienced and well-respected graduate recruiters, plus a full analysis of the current graduate job market, with details of the latest graduate starting salaries available.

In the quarter of a century since it was first published, more than 1.5 million copies of *The Times Top 100 Graduate Employers* have now been produced, helping students and graduates at universities across the UK to research their career options and find their first graduate job. Over 750,000 job hunters have registered to use *The Times Top 100 Graduate Employers* website – and during the past four years, more than 200,000 students and graduates have read the popular new digital edition of the *Top 100* that was introduced to accompany the print edition.

Some two and a half decades after its launch, *The Times Top 100 Graduate Employers* continues to provide an unrivalled, independent assessment of the UK's most highly-rated graduate employers.

THE TIMES TOP 100 GRADUATE EMPLOYERS

Finding out about the Top 100 Graduate Employers

PRINT EDITION

Each employer featured in this edition of the *Top 100* has their own **Employer Entry**, providing details of graduate vacancies for 2025, minimum academic requirements, starting salaries, for new graduates, plus this year's application deadlines.

DIGITAL EDITION

You'll find the **digital edition** of the *Top 100* on the official *Top 100* website, giving you access to the very latest information about the UK's most sought-after graduate employers..

Get ready for your graduate job search with full details of employers' forthcoming application deadlines.

And register on the website to receive regular updates about the country's top graduate employers.

www.Top100GraduateEmployers.com

BY EMAIL

Once you've registered with the *Top 100* website, you'll receive **weekly email bulletins** with news of the employers you're interested in, details of their latest graduate vacancies, and their application deadlines.

"A big part of Capgemini is growing your own career,
getting involved and adding value to projects that excite you. I really enjoy being organised and writing, so I was fortunate to be brought into bid management & given projects that suited and pushed my abilities."
For information on our graduate programmes
Scan here
Capgemini
Rewrite your future. Join us.

Transform your future

pwc

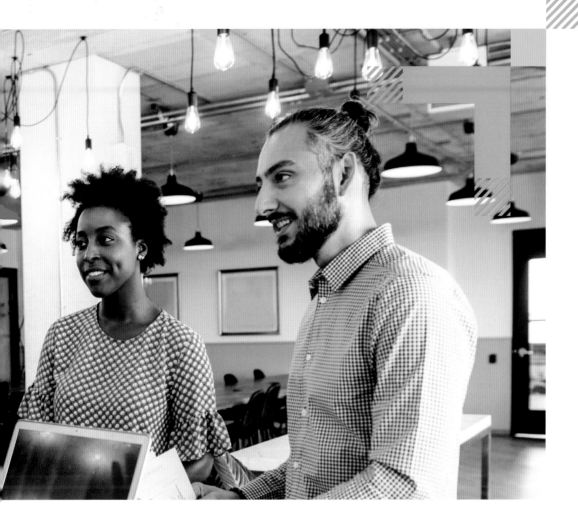

THE TIMES
TOP 100 GRADUATE EMPLOYERS 2016-2017
THE TIMES
TOP 100 GRADUATE EMPLOYERS 2017-2018
THE TIMES
TOP 100 GRADUATE EMPLOYERS 2018-2019
THE TIMES
TOP 100 GRADUATE EMPLOYERS 2019-2020
THE TIMES
TOP 100 GRADUATE EMPLOYERS 2020-2021
THE TIMES
TOP 100 GRADUATE EMPLOYERS 2021-2022
THE TIMES
TOP 100 GRADUATE EMPLOYERS 2022-2023
THE TIMES
TOP 100 GRADUATE EMPLOYERS 2023-2024
THE TIMES
TOP 100 GRADUATE EMPLOYERS 2024-2025

Researching The Times Top 100 Graduate Employers

By **Gill Thomas**
Publisher, High Fliers Publications

When the first edition of *The Times Top 100 Graduate Employers* was published in 1999, there were an estimated five thousand employers, large and small, recruiting graduates from UK universities.

The number of employers recruiting graduates has risen steadily in the past two and a half decades, and for those due to leave university in 2025 and beyond, there are expected to be more than 200,000 graduate-level vacancies available annually.

For students researching their career options, finding the 'right' graduate employer can often be a daunting prospect. What basis can you use to evaluate such a large number of different organisations and the employment opportunities they offer for new graduates after university?

The Times Top 100 Graduate Employers is compiled annually by the independent market research company, High Fliers Research, through interviews with final year students at the country's leading universities.

This latest edition is based on research with 14,271 students who were due to graduate from universities across the UK in the summer of 2024. The research examined students' experiences during their search for a first graduate job and asked them about their attitudes to employers.

THE TIMES TOP 100 GRADUATE EMPLOYERS

"The accounting & professional services firm PwC has retained its place as the UK's leading graduate employer."

Final year undergraduates from the 'Class of 2024' who took part in the study were selected at random to represent the full cross-section of finalists at their universities, not just those who had already confirmed their career plans and secured graduate employment.

The question used to produce the *Top 100* rankings was "Which employer do you think offers the best opportunities for graduates?". The question was deliberately open-ended and students were not shown a list of employers to choose from or prompted during the interview.

The wide selection of answers given during the research shows that final year students used very different criteria to decide which employer offered the best opportunities for graduates.

Some evaluated employers based on the quality of the recruitment promotions they'd seen whilst at university – either online or in-person – or their recent experiences during the application and graduate selection process.

Other final year students focused on the 'graduate employment proposition' as their main guide – the quality of training and development an employer offers, the starting salary and remuneration package available, and the practical aspects of a first graduate job, such as its location or the likely working hours.

THE TIMES TOP 100 GRADUATE EMPLOYERS

The Times Top 100 Graduate Employers 2024

	2023			2023	
1	1	PWC	51	22	UNLOCKED GRADUATES
2	2	CIVIL SERVICE	52	80	SHELL
3	3	NHS	53	47	BRITISH ARMY
4	4	DELOITTE	54	69	UBS
5	7	BBC	55	74	MI5 - THE SECURITY SERVICE
6	6	EY	56	45	HERBERT SMITH FREEHILLS
7	11	J.P. MORGAN	57	64	WHITE & CASE
8	5	GOOGLE	58	60	BLOOMBERG
9	10	BARCLAYS	59	97	ENTERPRISE MOBILITY
10	9	ALDI	60	57	LOCAL GOVERNMENT
11	8	KPMG	61	58	CLYDE & CO
12	20	LLOYDS BANKING GROUP	62	86	LATHAM & WATKINS
13	13	HSBC	63	62	AECOM
14	16	GOLDMAN SACHS	64	73	M&S
15	15	TEACH FIRST	65	75	BANK OF AMERICA
16	17	CLIFFORD CHANCE	66	83	BRITISH AIRWAYS
17	25	ASTRAZENECA	67	42	AIRBUS
18	18	MCKINSEY & COMPANY	68	55	TESCO
19	19	L'ORÉAL	69	68	BDO
20	14	GSK	70	99	WSP
21	12	AMAZON	71	50	DYSON
22	29	ARUP	72	51	DLA PIPER
23	21	UNILEVER	73	61	SANTANDER
24	35	A&O SHEARMAN	74	82	AON
25	34	ROLLS-ROYCE	75	89	CITI
26	31	P&G	76	78	SIEMENS
27	28	BAE SYSTEMS	77	NEW	IRWIN MITCHELL
28	24	NEWTON	78	71	MCDONALD'S
29	36	NATWEST GROUP	79	54	BAIN & COMPANY
30	40	BP	80	81	BANK OF ENGLAND
31	23	LINKLATERS	81	NEW	ROYAL AIR FORCE
32	33	BCG	82	72	HOGAN LOVELLS
33	43	POLICE NOW	83	84	MOTT MACDONALD
34	32	MORGAN STANLEY	84	NEW	TRANSPORT FOR LONDON
35	38	IBM	85	52	VODAFONE
36	39	PENGUIN	86	92	SECRET INTELLIGENCE SERVICE (MI6)
37	79	BLACKROCK	87	93	JACOBS
38	27	APPLE	88	NEW	BMW GROUP
39	48	ROYAL NAVY	89	67	BT GROUP
40	49	PFIZER	90	NEW	NESTLÉ
41	46	ATKINSRÉALIS	91	NEW	OLIVER WYMAN
42	59	JLR	92	77	BAKER MCKENZIE
43	41	SKY	93	94	FORVIS MAZARS
44	30	MICROSOFT	94	96	MARS
45	44	FRESHFIELDS	95	98	CAPGEMINI
46	NEW	ITV	96	70	DEUTSCHE BANK
47	53	ACCENTURE	97	76	SAVILLS
48	26	LIDL	98	90	GRANT THORNTON
49	37	SLAUGHTER AND MAY	99	NEW	ARM
50	56	JANE STREET	100	NEW	DIAGEO

Source High Fliers Research 14,271 final year students leaving UK universities in the summer of 2024 were asked the open-ended question "Which employer do you think offers the best opportunities for graduates?" during interviews for *The UK Graduate Careers Survey 2024*

Across the full survey sample, final year students named more than 1,500 different organisations, from well-known national and international organisations to small and medium-sized regional and local employers. The responses were analysed and the one hundred organisations that were named most often make up *The Times Top 100 Graduate Employers* for 2024.

In one of the closest votes in the twenty-six year history of the annual rankings, the accounting & professional services firm PwC has retained its place as the UK's leading graduate employer for the second year running, but by the narrowest of margins. This is the seventeenth time that the firm has been the country's number one graduate employer and 6 per cent of final year students from the 'Class of 2024' voted for the firm.

After four years as the number one graduate employer, the Civil Service – best-known for its prestigious Fast Stream programme – moved down into second place in 2023 and despite a substantial increase in its vote this year, it remains at number two in 2024 too. The NHS and the accounting & professional services firms Deloitte and EY are each unchanged in third, fourth and sixth places respectively.

The BBC has moved into the top five, its best ranking for seventeen years, and J.P. Morgan is ranked in seventh place, the highest-ever position for an investment bank in *Top 100*. Google has dropped back to eighth place, its lowest for a decade, but Barclays is up again, ahead of the retailer Aldi which is in tenth place this year.

KPMG, the accounting & professional services firm, has slipped out of the top ten for the first time, but Lloyds Banking Group climbs to 12th place – the bank's best ranking yet – up from 40th place just three years ago. Pharmaceuticals company AstraZeneca has returned to the top twenty, in its highest- ever position, overtaking rivals GSK which has dropped back to 20th place. And Amazon, which was one of the fastest-climbing employers ever in *The Times Top 100 Graduate Employers*, has fallen out of the top twenty this year.

Within the new *Top 100*, the year's highest climbers are led by the investment managers BlackRock, which has leapt forty-two places to 37th place, up from 79th place in 2023. Enterprise Mobility, the car and van hire company, has had a similar rise, jumping thirty-eight places to 59th place. Engineering consultants WSP, oil & energy company Shell and law firm Latham & Watkins are each up more than twenty places in this year's *Top 100*.

Vodafone has had the most significant fall of the year, dropping thirty-three places from 52nd place in 2023 to 85th place and the Unlocked prison officers programme, which was last year's highest-climber, has dropped back twenty-nine places to 51st place. Other graduate employers ranked lower in 2024 include Deutsche Bank, consultants Bain & Company and Airbus, who have each fallen at least twenty-five places this year.

For the first time ever, there are no new entries this year, but nine previously-ranked employers have re-entered the *Top 100*, the highest being for television company ITV, which returns in 46th place. Law firm Irwin Mitchell reappears in 77th place and, following a three- year absence, the RAF is ranked again, in 81st place in 2024. There are a further six re-entries, for Transport for London, the BMW Group, consumer goods company Nestlé, consultants Oliver Wyman, computing company Arm, and the multinational drinks giant Diageo.

With all three of the Armed Forces in the new *Top 100*, it is interesting to see that for the first time in twenty-six years, the Royal Navy – which is now in 42nd place – has been ranked ahead of the British Army, which has dropped to its lowest-ever ranking of 53rd place.

Among the graduate employers departing the *Top 100* in 2024 are Frontline, the children's social work graduate programme, which is unranked for the first time since its launch a decade ago. Other employers leaving the rankings this year include law firm CMS, Channel 4, technology consultants Kubrick, consumer goods manufacturers Johnson & Johnson, Mercedes, Cancer Research UK, engineering consultants Arcadis, and insurance company Aviva.

Since the original edition of *The Times Top 100 Graduate Employers* was published a quarter of a century ago, just three organisations have made it to number one in the rankings.

Andersen Consulting (now Accenture) held on to the top spot for the first four years, beginning in 1999, and its success heralded a huge surge in popularity for careers in consulting. At its peak in 2001, almost one in six graduates applied for jobs in the sector.

In the year before the firm changed its name from Andersen Consulting to Accenture, it astutely introduced a new graduate package that included a £28,500 starting salary (a sky-high

figure for graduates in 2000) and a much-talked-about £10,000 bonus, helping to assure the firm's popularity, irrespective of its corporate branding.

In 2003, after two dismal years in graduate recruitment when vacancies for university-leavers dropped by more than a fifth following the 9/11 terrorist attacks in 2001, the Civil Service was named the UK's leading graduate employer.

Just twelve months later it was displaced by PricewaterhouseCoopers, the accounting and professional services firm formed from the merger of Price Waterhouse and Coopers & Lybrand in 1998. At the time, the firm was the largest private sector recruiter of graduates, with an intake in 2004 of more than a thousand trainees.

Now known simply as PwC, the firm remained at number one for an impressive fifteen years, increasing its share of the student vote from 5 per cent in 2004 to more than 10 per cent in 2007, and fighting off the stiffest of competition from rivals Deloitte in 2008, when just seven votes separated the two employers.

PwC's reign as the UK's leading graduate employer represented a real renaissance for the entire accounting & professional services sector. Twenty years ago, a career in accountancy was often regarded as a safe, traditional employment choice, whereas today's profession is viewed in a very different light. The training required to become a chartered accountant is now seen as a prized business qualification, and the sector's leading firms are regularly described as 'dynamic' and 'international' by undergraduates looking for their first job after university – and continue to dominate the annual graduate employer rankings.

A total of 237 different organisations have now appeared within *The Times Top 100 Graduate Employers* since its inception, and thirty-six of these graduate employers hold the inspiring record of being ranked within the *Top 100* in all twenty-six editions since 1999.

The most consistent performers have been PwC, KPMG and the Civil Service, each of which have never been lower than 10th place in the league table. The NHS has also had a formidable record, appearing in every top ten since 2003, while the

THE TIMES TOP 100 GRADUATE EMPLOYERS

Number Ones, Movers & Shakers in the Top 100

NUMBER ONES		HIGHEST CLIMBING EMPLOYERS		HIGHEST NEW ENTRIES	
1999	ANDERSEN CONSULTING	1999	SCHLUMBERGER (UP 13 PLACES)	1999	PFIZER (31st)
2000	ANDERSEN CONSULTING	2000	CAPITAL ONE (UP 32 PLACES)	2000	MORGAN STANLEY (34th)
2001	ACCENTURE	2001	EUROPEAN COMMISSION (UP 36 PLACES)	2001	MARCONI (36th)
2002	ACCENTURE	2002	WPP (UP 36 PLACES)	2002	GUINNESS UDV (44th)
2003	CIVIL SERVICE	2003	ROLLS-ROYCE (UP 37 PLACES)	2003	ASDA (40th)
2004	PRICEWATERHOUSECOOPERS	2004	J.P. MORGAN (UP 29 PLACES)	2004	BAKER & MCKENZIE (61st)
2005	PRICEWATERHOUSECOOPERS	2005	TEACH FIRST (UP 22 PLACES)	2005	PENGUIN (70th)
2006	PRICEWATERHOUSECOOPERS	2006	GOOGLE (UP 32 PLACES)	2006	FUJITSU (81st)
2007	PRICEWATERHOUSECOOPERS	2007	PFIZER (UP 30 PLACES)	2007	BDO STOY HAYWARD (74th)
2008	PRICEWATERHOUSECOOPERS	2008	CO-OPERATIVE GROUP (UP 39 PLACES)	2008	SKY (76th)
2009	PRICEWATERHOUSECOOPERS	2009	CADBURY (UP 48 PLACES)	2009	BDO STOY HAYWARD (68th)
2010	PRICEWATERHOUSECOOPERS	2010	ASDA (UP 41 PLACES)	2010	SAATCHI & SAATCHI (49th)
2011	PWC	2011	CENTRICA (UP 41 PLACES)	2011	APPLE (53rd)
2012	PWC	2012	NESTLÉ (UP 44 PLACES)	2012	EUROPEAN COMMISSION (56th)
2013	PWC	2013	DFID (UP 40 PLACES)	2013	SIEMENS (70th)
2014	PWC	2014	TRANSPORT FOR LONDON (UP 36 PLACES)	2014	FRONTLINE (76th)
2015	PWC	2015	DIAGEO, NEWTON (UP 43 PLACES)	2015	DANONE (66th)
2016	PWC	2016	BANK OF ENGLAND (UP 34 PLACES)	2016	SANTANDER (63rd)
2017	PWC	2017	CANCER RESEARCH UK (UP 38 PLACES)	2017	DYSON (52nd)
2018	PWC	2018	MCDONALD'S (UP 30 PLACES)	2018	ASOS (52nd)
2019	CIVIL SERVICE	2019	POLICE NOW (UP 43 PLACES)	2019	UNLOCKED (49th)
2020	CIVIL SERVICE	2020	DLA PIPER/WHITE & CASE (UP 32 PLACES)	2020	CHANNEL FOUR (77th)
2021	CIVIL SERVICE	2021	CHARITYWORKS (UP 45 PLACES)	2021	BDO (49th)
2022	CIVIL SERVICE	2022	JAGUAR LAND ROVER (UP 30 PLACES)	2022	BMW GROUP (66th)
2023	PWC	2023	UNLOCKED (UP 45 PLACES)	2023	DLA PIPER (51st)
2024	PWC	2024	BLACKROCK (UP 42 PLACES)	2024	ITV (46th)

Source High Fliers Research

BBC and EY (formerly Ernst & Young) have both remained within the top twenty throughout the past twenty-five years. And consumer goods company Unilever and investment bank Goldman Sachs are two more employers that have appeared in the top quarter of the rankings each year.

Retailer Tesco is the highest-climbing employer within the *Top 100*, having risen eighty-eight places in its first thirteen years in the rankings, reaching 12th place in 2012. Google is another graduate employer that made very rapid progress during its early years in the *Top 100* rankings, jumping over eighty places in a decade, to reach the top three for the first time in 2015. But car manufacturer Jaguar Land Rover holds the record for the fastest-moving employer, after leaping more than seventy places in just five years, between 2009 and 2014.

Other well-known graduate employers haven't been so successful. British Airways ranked in 6th place in 1999 but dropped out of the *Top 100* a decade later, and Ford, which was once rated as high as 14th, disappeared out of the list in 2006 after cancelling its graduate recruitment programme two years previously. Sainsbury's appeared in the top twenty in both 2003 and 2004 but left the *Top 100* eight years ago and hasn't been ranked since.

More recent high-ranking casualties include the John Lewis Partnership which – having been 9th in 2003 – tumbled out of the *Top 100* in 2020 and Boots, the pharmacy and health retailer that initially appeared in 10th place in the first edition of *The Times Top 100 Graduate Employers* disappeared from the rankings in 2021. ExxonMobil, the oil & energy company that was a top twenty employer in the original *Top 100*, has also been unranked since 2021. And Marks & Spencer which was in 7th place in the inaugural Top 100 in 1999, dropped out of the rankings altogether in 2022.

More than thirty graduate employers – including

THE TIMES TOP 100 GRADUATE EMPLOYERS

Winners & Losers in the Top 100

EMPLOYERS CLIMBING HIGHEST	NEW ENTRY RANKING	HIGHEST RANKING
TESCO	**100th** (1999)	**12th** (2012)
GOOGLE	**85th** (2005)	**3rd** (2015)
LIDL	**89th** (2009)	**13th** (2017)
NEWTON	**94th** (2013)	**19th** (2019)
AMAZON	**81st** (2015)	**10th** (2022)
JAGUAR LAND ROVER	**87th** (2009)	**16th** (2014)
ALDI	**65th** (2002)	**2nd** (2015-2016)
MI5 - THE SECURITY SERVICE	**96th** (2007)	**33rd** (2010)
POLICE NOW	**90th** (2018)	**28th** (2021)
TEACH FIRST	**63rd** (2003)	**2nd** (2014)
APPLE	**87th** (2009)	**27th** (2012)
DEUTSCHE BANK	**81st** (1999)	**23rd** (2005)
ATKINS	**94th** (2004)	**37th** (2009)
SLAUGHTER AND MAY	**90th** (2001)	**36th** (2022)
FRONTLINE	**76th** (2014)	**26th** (2018)
EMPLOYERS FALLING FURTHEST	**HIGHEST RANKING**	**LOWEST RANKING**
BRITISH AIRWAYS	**6th** (1999)	**Not ranked** (2010, 2011, 2017, 2019-2022)
MARKS & SPENCER	**7th** (1999)	**Not ranked** (2021-2022)
JOHN LEWIS PARTNERSHIP	**9th** (2013)	**Not ranked** (FROM 2020)
BOOTS	**10th** (1999)	**Not ranked** (FROM 2021)
FORD	**11th** (1999)	**Not ranked** (FROM 2006)
UBS	**17th** (2002)	**Not ranked** (2018)
SAINSBURY'S	**18th** (2003)	**Not ranked** (FROM 2016)
EXXONMOBIL	**19th** (1999)	**Not ranked** (FROM 2021)
SHELL	**11th** (2006)	**90th** (2021)
THOMSON REUTERS	**22nd** (2001)	**Not ranked** (2009-2012, FROM 2014)
FRONTLINE	**26th** (2018)	**Not ranked** (2024)
BANK OF AMERICA	**27th** (2000)	**Not ranked** (FROM 2017-2020)
ASDA	**27th** (2004)	**Not ranked** (FROM 2018)
RAF	**32nd** (2005)	**Not ranked** (2015, FROM 2021)
CANCER RESEARCH UK	**34th** (2008)	**Not ranked** (2019-2022, 2024)

Source High Fliers Research

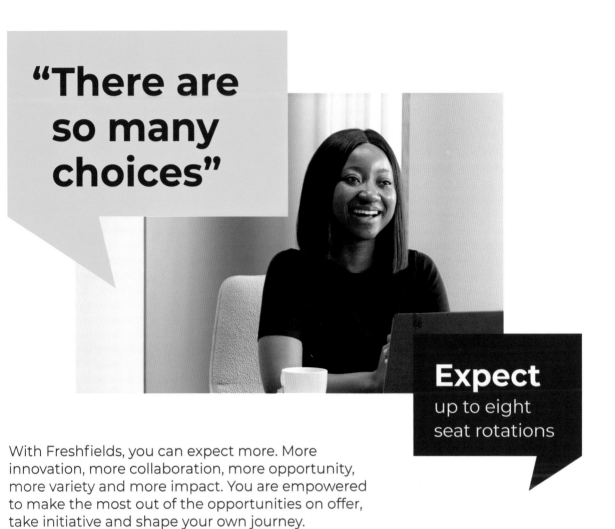

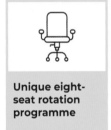

Nokia, Maersk, the Home Office, Cable & Wireless, United Biscuits, Nationwide, Samsung, Mercedes, the Met Office and TikTok – have the dubious record of having only been ranked in the *Top 100* once during the last twenty-six years. And former engineering & telecommunications company Marconi had the unusual distinction of being one of the highest-ever new entries, in 36th place in 2001, only to vanish from the list entirely the following year.

One of the most spectacular ascendancies in the Top 100 has been the rise of Aldi, which joined the list in 65th place in 2002, rose to 3rd place in 2009 – helped in part by its memorable remuneration package for new recruits (currently £50,000 plus a fully-expensed VW electric car) – and was ranked in 2nd place in both 2015 and 2016. Consulting firm Newton is another impressive climber, having jumped more than seventy places from 94th place in 2013 to being ranked in the top twenty for the first time in 2019.

The Coronavirus pandemic had a very significant impact on the annual rankings, with a fifth of the employers that appeared in *The Times Top 100 Graduate Employers* in 2020 – the final rankings before the onset of the pandemic – no longer ranked two years later.

Teach First, the first of five inspirational schemes that are transforming society by bringing top graduates into public service, appeared as a new entry in 63rd place in 2003, before climbing the rankings every year for a decade and reaching

THE TIMES TOP 100 GRADUATE EMPLOYERS

Employers Ranked from 1999-2024 in the Top 100

MOST CONSISTENT EMPLOYERS	HIGHEST RANKING	LOWEST RANKING
PWC	**1st** (2004-2018, 2023-2024)	**3rd** (1999-2001, 2003, 2022)
CIVIL SERVICE	**1st** (2003, 2019-2022)	**8th** (2011)
KPMG	**3rd** (2006-2008, 2011-2012)	**11th** (2024)
BBC	**5th** (2005-2007, 2024)	**14th** (1999)
GSK	**10th** (2017-2018)	**22nd** (2002-2003)
EY (FORMERLY ERNST & YOUNG)	**6th** (2021-2023)	**20th** (2001)
GOLDMAN SACHS	**5th** (2001)	**25th** (1999)
HSBC	**6th** (2003)	**29th** (1999)
BARCLAYS	**9th** (2024)	**35th** (2006)
NHS	**2nd** (2022)	**27th** (1999, 2002)
UNILEVER	**7th** (2002)	**23rd** (2008)
BAE SYSTEMS	**23rd** (1999)	**49th** (2015)
DELOITTE	**2nd** (2013)	**30th** (2001)
BP	**14th** (2003-2004)	**42th** (2021)
CLIFFORD CHANCE	**16th** (2024)	**45th** (2007, 2012)
McKINSEY & COMPANY	**18th** (2022-2023)	**48th** (2008)
IBM	**13th** (2000)	**46th** (2022)
ALLEN & OVERY	**24th** (2010, 2024)	**57th** (2005)
PROCTER & GAMBLE	**4th** (1999-2001)	**39th** (2022)
MICROSOFT	**21st** (2004-2005)	**58th** (1999)
J.P. MORGAN	**7th** (2024)	**45th** (2003)
ARUP	**22nd** (2024)	**60th** (2001)
LINKLATERS	**19th** (2021)	**59th** (2000)
LLOYDS BANKING GROUP	**12th** (2024)	**56th** (2001)
BRITISH ARMY	**4th** (2003)	**53rd** (2024)
ACCENTURE	**1st** (1999-2002)	**53rd** (2023)
ROLLS-ROYCE	**15th** (2019)	**68th** (2002)
ROYAL NAVY	**35th** (2010)	**88th** (2013)
CITI	**30th** (2008)	**89th** (2023)
L'ORÉAL	**19th** (2022-2023)	**85th** (2018)
McDONALD'S	**29th** (2003)	**98th** (2016-2017)
DEUTSCHE BANK	**23rd** (2005)	**96th** (2018)
BT	**14th** (2000)	**89th** (2024)
SHELL	**11th** (2006)	**90th** (2021)
MARS	**9th** (2000)	**96th** (2023)
TESCO	**12th** (2012)	**100th** (1999)

Source High Fliers Research

Do great minds think alike
or completely differently?
At HSBC, diversity isn't a buzzword. It's essential. That's why we encourage applications to our Global Internships and Graduate Programmes from students and graduates with any degree, from any background.
hsbc.com/earlycareers
HSBC

2nd place in the Top 100 in 2014. Frontline, the children's social work graduate programme, was a new entry in 76th place that year, before progressing fifty places to 26th place by 2018. Over the past six years, another of these programmes, Police Now, jumped more than sixty places from 90th in 2018 to 28th place in the *Top 100* in 2021.

And most-recently, Unlocked – the ground-breaking programme recruiting graduates to work as prison officers – reached 22nd place in 2023, just four years after it first joined the *Top 100* as a new entry in 2019.

Together, the twenty-six annual editions of *The Times Top 100 Graduates Employers* have produced a definitive record of the graduate employers that generations of students and recent graduates have aspired to join after leaving university – and these latest results provide a unique insight into how the 'Class of 2024' rated the country's leading graduate employers.

THE TIMES TOP 100 GRADUATE EMPLOYERS

The UK's Number 1 Graduate Employer 2024

"We are incredibly proud and delighted to be number one in *The Times Top 100 Graduate Employers* for the second year running – and the seventeenth time overall.

We work hard to make sure the opportunities that we offer to students and graduates are compelling and that the firm is a great place to begin your career and develop in the future.

Each year, we spend a great deal of time on campus introducing PwC to students in all years, from all backgrounds and studying all degree disciplines – and giving potential applicants a real feel for the culture of our firm and its people.

We know that making the right career choice is a big decision. If you're looking for a taster experience, a work placement, or are thinking of applying for a graduate position with us, we want you to have the chance to meet us in-person, so you can make an informed decision about your options.

We collaborate with university careers services and student societies to run an extensive programme of events, skills sessions and experiences at universities around the country. Our aim is to help you understand the breadth of opportunities you get working for a firm like ours – look out for our distinctive 'eco-booth' at your university during the year ahead.

Making the transition from education into the workplace can be really challenging. PwC recruits up to 1,500 graduates each year in the UK and whichever part of the firm you join after university, we want you to have the best possible start to your career. You'll be supported by world-class professional training, careers coaches, and a large peer-group of like-minded graduates.

PWC

Cathy Baxter, Head of Early Careers, PwC

From preparing to become a chartered accountant or tax adviser, to developing as a business consultant or technology specialist, we provide unrivalled opportunities for new graduates to hone their technical and professional skills.

And for those with an eye on the future, our graduate programmes can be the foundation for fulfilling careers at the firm. But they also provide qualifications and training & development that is recognised and respected across the wider employment market.

So whether you opt to stay with the firm long-term or move into roles elsewhere, your early experiences as a graduate with PwC will help shape your career."

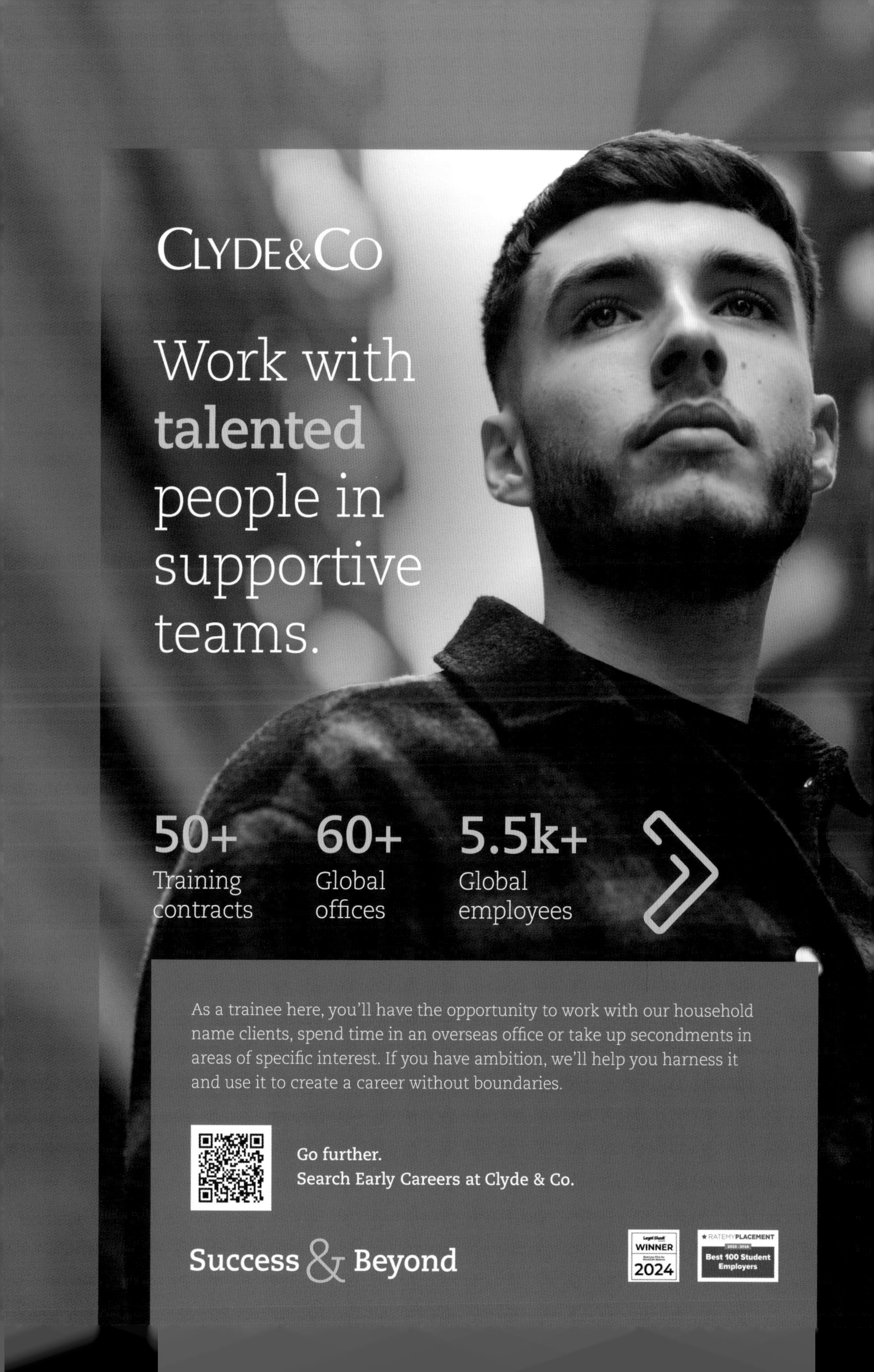
CLYDE&CO
Work with talented people in supportive teams.
50+
Training contracts
60+
Global offices
5.5k+
Global employees
As a trainee here, you'll have the opportunity to work with our household name clients, spend time in an overseas office or take up secondments in areas of specific interest. If you have ambition, we'll help you harness it and use it to create a career without boundaries.
Go further.
Search Early Careers at Clyde & Co.
Success & Beyond
WINNER
2024
RATEMYPLACEMENT
Best 100 Student Employers

SCHOOL

Gen Z will only work from home

By **Lucy Johnston**
SOCIAL AFFAIRS EDITOR

MORE than half of younger workers would turn down a job unless it allowed them to work from home.

A survey of adults aged 18-42 – taking in Generation Z and millennials – demonstrates how attitudes to work have shifted in recent years.

Many of the 5,000 people polled had begun their careers working from home during the pandemic.

More than half said they suffered from workplace stress, and nearly ...

about health and wellbeing, and are passionate about finding a job that aligns with their personal values.

"Flexibility is hugely motivating, which employers must consider when attracting and retaining talent."

Debbie Porter, managing director at Destination Digital Marketing, said: "Over the last couple of years I've had university graduates request ...

Graduate recruitment down as vacancies plunge by 30pc

... search engine Adzuna show that UK ...

'We students are finding ways to fight back against AI interviews'

With up to 100 people for each graduate job, AI is being used to cut candidates. One ...

British graduates suffering as internships dry up

By **Eir Nolsøe**

... to secure an ... highest mar... high inter... market. ... al that the ... tive to job ... in recent ... r than at ...

even though the US jobs held up better than the UK.

Jack Kennedy, Indeed, said that while hiring in the ... robust for many lower-pa... roles, higher-paid sector... encing a more pronounce...

He added: "We have hea... about a kind of white-colla...

"Our sectoral job-postin... corroborate that."

1.8million have at least £50,000 of student debt

loans are means tested, so people from the poorest backgrounds end up in the most debt,' she said.

'They also generally pay back loans slower, and end up paying more in interest.' Ms Field added that 'essentially, working class ...

'Penalises the poorest'

'is not working well because these people will not pay it all back'.

A senior electrical engineer from Croydon said his student debt – which stands at £128,200 – rose by £788 between April and June due to interest. The huge debt was racked up during a four-year course at London South Bank University and two years studying for a Higher National Diploma.

The 43-year-old, who did not want to be identified, told the ...

awarded on a sliding scale depending on parental income.

Graduates repay 9 per cent of anything earned over £27,295, and after 30 years any debt remaining is wiped. But for those starting university this year ...

Graduates struggle to get work as employers cut back

Kristy Dorsey

NEARLY two-thirds of all recent graduates are struggling to find relevant work amid signs that employers are continuing to cut back on recruitment in this area.

In a new poll from specialist recruitment firm ...

Not Mickey Mouse degrees after all!

Games designers earn more than law graduates

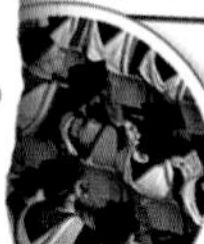

average of £30,500. Other traditional degrees that fell short were education from Cambridge University with £31,000, history at Edinburgh with £31,500 and biochemistry at Exeter with ...

thing to do but it's not the only route." His Nottingham Trent institute offers degrees such as e-sports, virtual production and content creation.

Music production graduate Gaddiel Nketia, 23, said he earned between £25,000 and £30,000 in his first year as a self-employed composer ...

ents as a safe choice – but I just knew I wanted to give it a shot, and it has been so rewarding.

"If you go into university with a ready-to-learn attitude, meet people and don't shy away, you can take away so much more."

Graduate salaries in finance sector power ahead

Demand strong for courses despite dis... write *Andrew Jack, Leo Cremonezi* and ...

Salaries for graduates of leading masters in finance programmes have grown much faster for those working in financial services compared with other sectors, in a sign of the industry's strength.

Surge in number of graduates stuck in jobs not needing a degree

By **Eir Nolsøe**

LARGE swathes of overqualified graduates outside London are stuck ...

analysis suggests that many young people are racking up tens of thousands of pounds in student debt without ...

ates end up in roles where a degree is superfluous, but this has remained stable over the past three decades.

42pc

University-educated workers outside London stuck in jobs not requiring a degree, up from 31pc since 1993

more than two decades of lost pay, as wages have stagnated.

In the US, early thirties workers are earning 21pc more than those born a decade earlier at the same age.

In contrast, Britons in the same age group are making less than their predecessors did at the same age before the financial crisis.

While the US has had far stronger wage growth than the UK, it has also ...

pointed out that, simulta... homeownership rates have ... 20 percentage points for 30 t... old Britons since 1986.

Over the same time, this ... only 3pc in the US.

Sophie Hale from the R... Foundation said: "The lack o... made by millennials in the ... how important it is to restart ... ful growth in the UK, but also ... that policy decisions recognis...

University graduates outside London stuck in low-skilled jobs

high concentration of graduate jobs in comparison to the rest of the UK damages the career opportunities of those who cannot afford to relocate.

The IFS said the number of low paid jobs has increased evenly across the UK over the last 20 years, while middle-range positions have disappeared in a process known as 'hollowing out'.

However, skilled jobs with high salaries, requiring a university degree, have mainly emerged in London. The trend means those who cannot afford to move to the capital to find work after university are less able to reap the returns of their higher education.

The number of university leavers in graduate jobs in inner Lon...

AI will enhance most jobs not steal them, says Google

Alex Hern ...

According to research from the thinktank Public First, commissioned by Google, 61% of British jobs will be "radically" transformed by AI, with just 31% "insulated" from the technology - defined as having less than a quarter of their workplace tasks with the potential to be automated.

Those insulated jobs would be overwhelmingly in social care, transport, accommodation, and food services, where complex and varied physical tasks were only achievable by human workers, Public First said.

Just a handful of jobs were likely to be fully "phased out" by AI, the thinktank estimated. Even the most affected sector, financial and insurance, is forecast to lose just 4% of jobs, with 83% "enhanced" instead.

Public First's findings are similar to research from the Tony Blair Institute. Public First drew up its ...

'What's tricky ... that we actually ... know exactly wh... going to transpir...

Debbie Weinstein
MD of Google UK

AI to either significantly re... time taken to do them, or a... them entirely".

Google is partnering w... Community trade union, th... business network Enterprise... and a pair of multi-academ... to research how best to intro... technology into workplaces.

Weinstein said: "Part of ...

Skills shortage puts Britain's potential at risk

Gill Plimmer and Rachel Millard are entirely right ("Britain has big infrastructure plans. But where are the workers?", Report, June 4) to draw attention to the UK's critical skills shortage. We have the opportunity to harness growth through investing in green jobs and green industry, but ... have seen targets rolled ...

confidence in the UK at the very moment competitors abroad are straining every sinew, but it also stores up problems for the future. Companies in the construction sector, or adjacent to it, have to reduce investments and this curtails their ability to bring in early-career staff, be that graduates or apprentices. We are already seeing the ...

about the fact that not enough is being done to support these industries. In an ideal world, the skills gap issue would be above party politics, but instead it is being treated as a political football.

There is still a huge amount of potential in the UK and we shouldn't forget that. But equally, we need to remember that there is no inherent ...

Understanding the Graduate Job Market

By **Martin Birchall**
Managing Director, High Fliers Research

Over the past quarter of a century since the first edition of *The Times Top 100 Graduate Employers* was published in 1999, graduate recruitment at the UK's leading employers has increased very substantially.

The number of graduate vacancies on offer to university-leavers has increased in seventeen of the past twenty-five years and reached a new record level in 2022, with almost twice as many opportunities available, compared to graduate recruitment at the beginning of the new the millenium.

But this sustained period of growth in graduate jobs has been punctuated by four significant downturns in recruitment.

In the two years following the 9/11 terrorist attacks in the US, the worsening economic outlook prompted employers in the UK to reduce their entry-level vacancies for new graduates by more than 15 per cent.

Graduate recruitment recovered in 2004 and vacancies for university-leavers grew at between 10 and 12 per cent annually over the next three years, before the global financial crisis of 2008 and 2009 heralded the worst recession in the UK since the Second World War.

Graduate vacancies at the country's top employers plunged by an unprecedented 23 per cent in less than 18 months – and almost 10,000 jobs were cut or left unfilled from a planned intake of more than 40,000 new graduates during this period. A record fifty-nine of the employers featured in *The Times Top 100 Graduate Employers* reduced their graduate hiring in 2009 alone.

Although the graduate job market bounced back successfully in 2010, with an annual increase in vacancies of more than 12 per cent, it took a further five years for graduate recruitment to return to the pre-recession peak recorded in 2007.

"Accounting & professional services firms will be the largest recruiter of new graduates in 2025, with over 6,500 roles on offer."

The uncertainty that followed Britain's vote to leave the European Union in 2016 saw graduate vacancies dip again in 2017. But growth returned a year later and by 2019 entry-level recruitment was up by 43 per cent compared to the number of vacancies available in 2009 – the low point in graduate recruitment during the economic crisis – and had been expected to rise even higher in 2020.

But the start of the Coronavirus pandemic in March 2020 forced the UK's top employers to pause or re-evaluate their graduate recruitment and many were unable to continue with that year's planned annual intake of university-leavers.

Graduate recruitment was cut in thirteen out of fifteen industries and business sectors, most noticeably at major engineering & industrial companies and accounting & professional services firms, where over 700 planned vacancies were left unfilled. The final number of graduates recruited

DO,
DISCOVER,
DEVELOP.
Join Barclays as a graduate or intern, and you'll do work that challenges you, discover opportunities to stretch you and develop innovations that excite you. You'll enjoy the kind of training that will bring out the best in you. And you'll be empowered to discover your full potential.
To find out more, type search.jobs.barclays
BARCLAYS

by employers featured in *The Times Top 100 Graduate Employers* in 2020 was 12 per cent lower than in 2019.

Recruitment began to bounce back in 2021 with a substantial 9.4 per cent rise in entry-level vacancies – the 'V-shaped' pandemic recovery in the graduate job market largely mirroring the recovery in the wider economy.

This strong growth gathered pace the following year when graduate vacancies increased in all fifteen industries and business sectors represented in *The Times Top 100 Graduate Employers*. In all, the number of graduate jobs available jumped by 14.5 per cent in 2022, the largest-ever year-on-year rise in graduate recruitment at the UK's leading employers.

Over the past twelve months, recruitment has been stable, with a modest 1.5 per cent increase in graduate vacancies, and at the start of the new 2024-2025 recruitment season, employers in *The Times Top 100 Graduate Employers* are predicting that they will have a total of 26,043 graduate vacancies for autumn 2025 start dates.

This is a slight reduction in the number graduates recruited in 2024 – an annual decrease of 1.1 per cent – and suggests that employers have a cautious outlook and graduate recruitment is likely to be largely unchanged for the second consecutive year.

A fifth of employers are planning to hire more graduates in 2025, two fifths expect to match their previous intake, but over a third of organisations are likely to recruit fewer university-leavers over the coming year.

In 2023, accounting & professional services firms featured in the *Top 100* recruited an unprecedented number of university-leavers – a total of more than 7,000 trainees. And although recruitment in the past year has been lower, the sector will again be the largest recruiter of new graduates in 2025, with over 6,500 roles on offer.

Graduate vacancies in the public sector are expected to increase for the fourth consecutive year, with more than 4,200 entry level opportunities available. And after a sharp rise in recruitment at engineering & industrial companies in 2024, these employers are set to cut their graduate intake in 2025 by a fifth.

After a small rise in vacancies in 2024, there are expected to be fewer graduate roles at the City's investment banks and fund managers in 2025 and employers elsewhere in the banking and finance sector also expect to cut their recruitment.

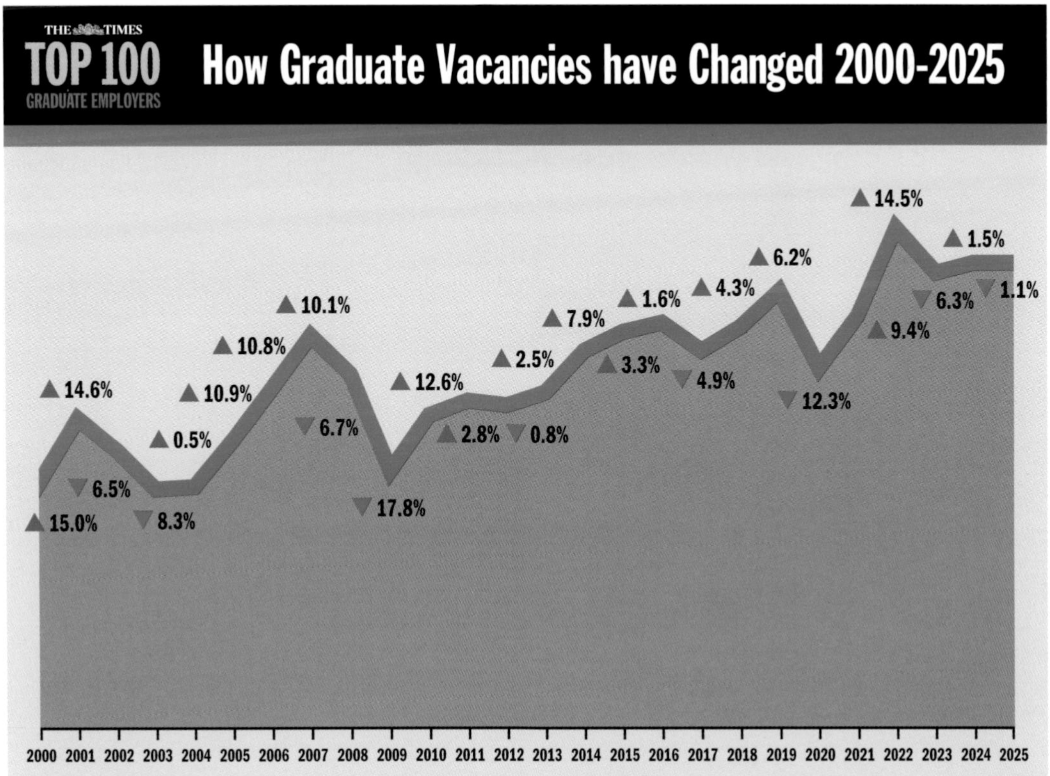

Source High Fliers Research

In the next 12 months, graduate recruitment is predicted to rise or match 2024 hiring levels in just six out of fifteen key industries and business sectors, with graduate vacancies expected to decrease in the remaining nine sectors.

The three employers from *The Times Top 100 Graduate Employers* with the biggest graduate recruitment targets for 2025 are Teach First, the popular programme that recruits graduates to teach in schools in low-income communities around the UK, which has 1,750 places available – and accounting & professional services firms PwC and Deloitte, which are each aiming to recruit 1,500 new trainees in the year ahead.

Other very substantial individual graduate recruiters in 2024 include the car & van rental company Enterprise Mobility (1,300 graduate vacancies), the Civil Service Fast Stream (1,000 vacancies) and accounting & professional services firms EY and KPMG (1,000 vacancies each).

Over half of *Top 100* employers have vacancies for graduates in technology and finance, two fifths have opportunities in engineering, and a third are recruiting for human resources roles, consulting positions, or general management vacancies.

At least a fifth of the country's top graduate employers are looking for new recruits to work in sales or marketing and research & development,

THE TIMES TOP 100 GRADUATE EMPLOYERS

Graduate Vacancies & Starting Salaries in 2025

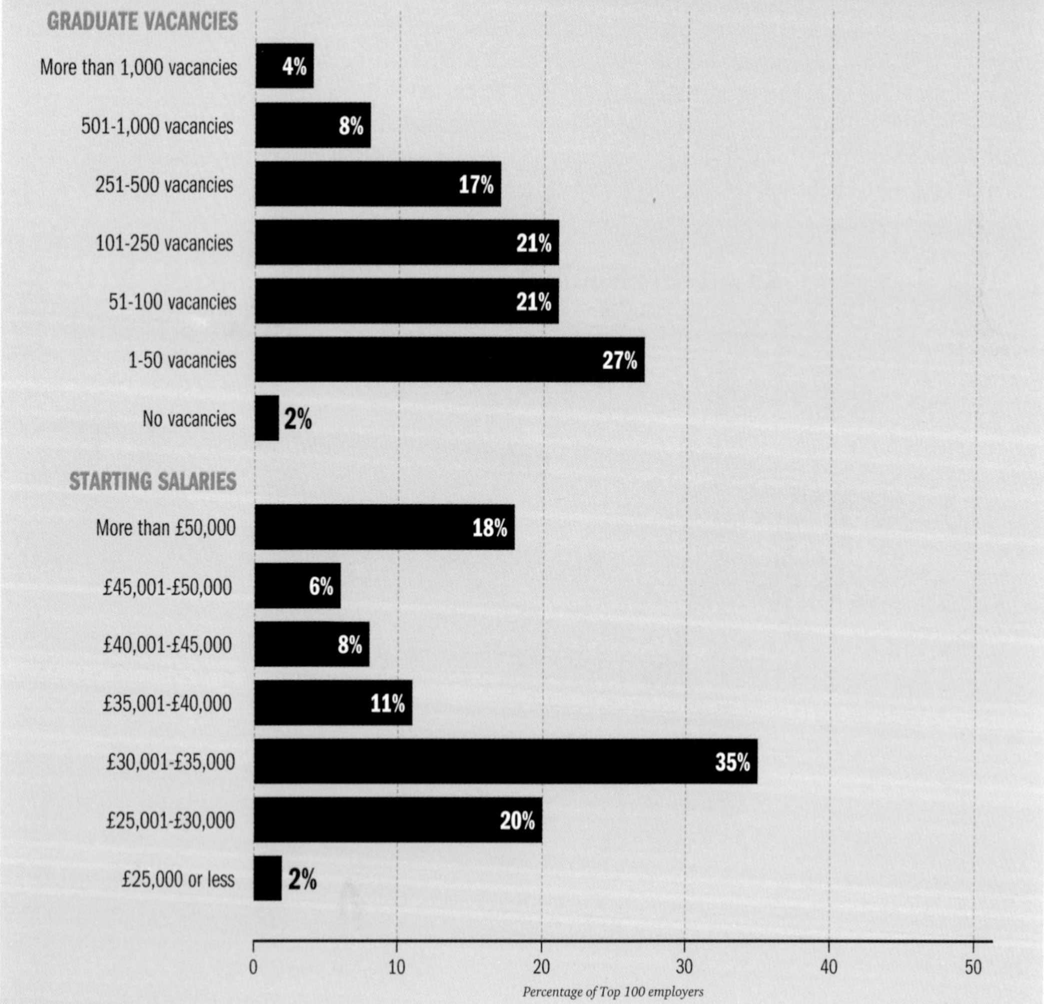

Source High Fliers Research

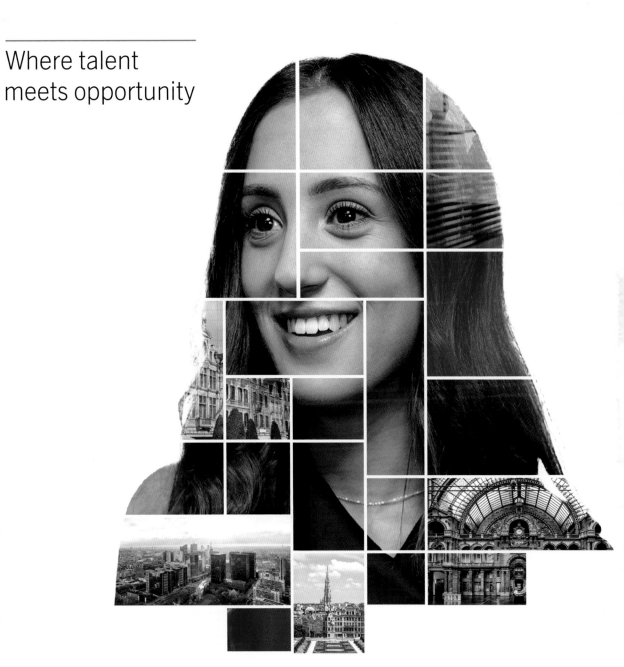

but there are fewer graduate jobs available in retailing or in more specialist areas, such as purchasing, logistics & supply chain, property and the media.

More than four-fifths of *Top 100* employers have graduate vacancies in London in 2025, and three-fifths have posts available elsewhere in the south east of England. Up to half also have roles in the north west of England, the south west, the Midlands, Yorkshire and the north east. Over half are recruiting for graduate roles in Scotland, but Northern Ireland, Wales and East Anglia have the fewest employers with vacancies this year.

Graduate starting salaries at *The Times Top 100 Graduate Employers* changed little between 2012 and 2021, increasing by just £1,000 in this nine-year period to a median of £30,000. But this went up to £32,000 in 2022, the first annual boost in starting salaries for seven years. And it has continued rising since – to £33,500 in 2023 and £34,000 in 2024.

These rates are expected to increase further in 2025, with the most generous starting salaries available at the leading investment banks & fund managers (a median of £60,000), law firms (£56,000) and consulting firms (£50,000).

It is noticeable that employers in each of these popular destinations for new graduates have opted to step-up their starting salaries in the past year, with record annual increases at several of the top City and international law firms.

One in six employers featured in *The Times Top 100 Graduate Employers* now offering starting salaries in excess of £50,000 for their new recruits. The most tempting salaries publicised within this edition are at the law firms A&O Shearman, Freshfields, Herbert Smith Freehills, Hogan Lovells, Linklaters, Slaughter and May, and White & Case – each of which is offering new trainees a starting salary of £56,000 in 2025.

Away from the legal sector, retailer Aldi continues to pay a sector-leading graduate salary of £50,000 for its Area Management trainee programme, and consulting firm Newton offers a starting salary of £45,000.

One in three of the UK's leading employers recruit graduates year-round, or in different phases during the year, and will accept applications throughout the 2024-2025 recruitment season until all their vacancies are filled. For employers with an annual application deadline, most are in November or December, although a limited number have October or post-Christmas deadlines for their graduate programmes.

This means that there is every incentive to apply early for the wide variety of graduate vacancies that are available in 2025 at *The Times Top 100 Graduate Employers*.

THE TIMES TOP 100 GRADUATE EMPLOYERS

Graduate Vacancies at Top 100 Employers in 2025

	2024		GRADUATE VACANCIES IN 2025	% CHANGE IN 2025	% CHANGE IN 2024	MEDIAN STARTING SALARY IN 2025
1.	1	ACCOUNTANCY & PROFESSIONAL SERVICES FIRMS	6,695	▲ 13.5%	▼ 8.2%	£37,500
2.	2	PUBLIC SECTOR EMPLOYERS	4,293	▲ 4.2%	▲ 9.4%	£30,300
3.	3	ENGINEERING & INDUSTRIAL COMPANIES	3,325	▼ 21.0%	▲ 20.8%	£30,900
4.	4	TECHNOLOGY COMPANIES	2,050	▼ 1.9%	▼ 10.6%	£33,500
5.	6	INVESTMENT BANKS & FUND MANAGERS	1,850	▼ 4.8%	▲ 4.1%	£60,000
6.	5	BANKING & FINANCIAL SERVICES	1,775	▼ 7.5%	▲ 3.9%	£35,000
7.	8	ARMED FORCES	1,350	NO CHANGE	▲ 3.0%	£31,000
8.	9	MEDIA ORGANISATIONS	975	▲ 21.4%	▼ 22.2%	£28,800
9.	7	LAW FIRMS	857	▼ 7.6%	▲ 7.8%	£56,000
10.	10	RETAILERS	415	▼ 3.5%	▲ 9.1%	£34,000
11.	13	CONSUMER GOODS MANUFACTURERS	275	▼ 9.8%	▲ 7.3%	£35,000
12.	11	CONSULTING FIRMS	260	▼ 20.7%	▼ 24.2%	£50,000
13.	12	OIL & ENERGY COMPANIES	250	▼ 1.6%	▲ 18.1%	£42,000
14.	14	CHEMICAL & PHARMACEUTICALS COMPANIES	143	▲ 9.2%	▼ 3.1%	£32,500
15.	-	PROPERTY COMPANIES	130	▲ 16.1%	▼ 14.5%	£27,500

Source High Fliers Research

MORE REWARDS
Earn a market leading salary of **£50,000** rising to **£94,240**

MORE BENEFITS
A fully expensed **electric car**, five weeks' holiday, healthcare and **more**

MORE DEVELOPMENT
Learn through our **12 month training plan** and dedicated mentors

MORE RESPONSIBILITY
Manage, coach and lead a **team** of over **100 colleagues**

WELCOME

Queen Mary
University of London
Welcome to
Careers and Enterprise
Reception

Successful Graduate Job Hunting

By **Judith Baines**
Head of Careers and Enterprise, Queen Mary University of London

Whichever career path you hope to take after you leave university, the sooner you begin exploring your options, the more likely you are to be successful.

For more than 70 per cent of graduate jobs, employers aren't looking for a specific qualification or degree course. You don't need to have studied finance in order to work as an accountant, roles in technology wouldn't necessarily require a computer science degree, and if you're hoping to become a consultant, you can do so without a degree in business or management.

This means employers usually recruit based on graduates' skills and abilities, not the content of what they've studied for their degree. Your 2.1 in history could lead to a career in marketing, a geography degree could be the starting point for a career in the Civil Service, and a psychology course might be followed by a graduate job as a tax adviser.

The choice is so wide – there are several thousand different graduate jobs, occupations and professions that you could pursue after graduation – it can be very daunting to know where to begin. For most students, the question isn't 'What can I do with my degree?' or 'Which graduate jobs am I qualified to do?', it's 'What type of career am I interested in?' and 'Do I have the necessary skills that employers are looking for?'.

THE TIMES TOP 100 GRADUATE EMPLOYERS

"The Times Top 100 Graduate Employers receive between 40 and 50 applications for each graduate vacancy."

If you can, you should start thinking about your future career in your first year. It may seem strange to be thinking about your post-university plans when you've only just arrived and are still settling into your new course, making friends and getting to grips with your studies. But those first few weeks and months are the ideal time to begin understanding the graduate job market and what you are interested in.

As a first step, you should make contact with your university careers service. Every university has its own careers service that offers students independent advice, guidance and information about graduate employment and other options for after university.

You can start by accessing their website to find out where in the university they are based and go along to see what your careers service offers. Many have teams of students working on reception and as guides, who can talk to you and show you round and explain the information and resources that are available.

When you're ready, you should book an appointment to see a careers adviser or consultant. Appointments are usually in-person within the careers service but can be online too, if that is more convenient.

This initial appointment is all about discovering what you need. Are you someone who has a clear

CHANGE
THE STORY
What if your actions could change society for the better?
As a neighbourhood police officer, you can stop crime before it happens. You can help communities rocked by injustice. You can build a better tomorrow.
Our two-year programme develops your leadership and problem-solving skills so that you can reduce crime and transform communities.
Join the only national graduate programme for neighbourhood policing.
POLICE:NOW
INFLUENCE FOR GENERATIONS
Scan to read Anokhi's story
or visit
policenow.org.uk
"When looking at how to make an impact in policing, I was pulled towards how I could improve it from the inside."
Anokhi Chouhan | Police Now Graduate
A starting salary of £28,551 - £36,775 depending on location.
A dedicated Performance and Development Coach to support you.
A peer network of over 3,000 Police Now officers.
A secondment opportunity inside or outside of policing in your second year.

idea about the types of jobs you're interested in and want to find out about employers' application and selection processes? Or are you one of the many who is just starting to think about what you could do in the future and has no clear idea about what that might be.

It's important to remember that your careers adviser won't give you all the answers about which jobs to apply for or the graduate employers that would be right for you – only you can make those decisions. But they can encourage you to understand your skills and interests and advise you on the different ways you can investigate your career options. Your appointment with a careers adviser is likely to be the first of several and each time they will give you an 'action plan' with the next steps to take.

One of the main advantages of getting in touch early with your university careers service is you'll discover the wide range of events, workshops and training sessions that they run during the year, to help you find out about different industries, business sectors and career areas – and the graduate employers within them.

Almost every careers service hosts their own careers fairs, usually during the autumn, and these are a great way to meet employers in-person and find out which organisations are actively promoting their graduate programmes.

Employers will often send new graduates back to their old university for these fairs, giving you the chance to meet recent alumni who can talk about what it's like to work there and the role they're doing. It can be a really good way to find out about what the culture of the organisation is like – and whether you could imagine working there.

If you're able to go to a careers fair in your first year, then you can find out about the 'taster experiences' or insight programme that many of the larger employers offer during the Easter holiday in your first year. These typically last between two days and a week and provide an in-depth introduction to an employer and their graduate roles. Applications for these courses usually close in December or January and most include a selection process for the available places.

Employers attending fairs will also provide information about their summer internships and other work experience schemes, as well as their graduate programmes.

To get the most out of a careers fair, it's important to do some research before the event itself. It's no good asking an employer what they do, or which type of jobs they offer, when all of that information is available on their website. Make the most of being able to speak to a recruiter or a recent graduate to ask them about what the organisation looks for in the graduates they recruit, and their

THE TIMES TOP 100 GRADUATE EMPLOYERS

Careers Information used by the 'Class of 2024'

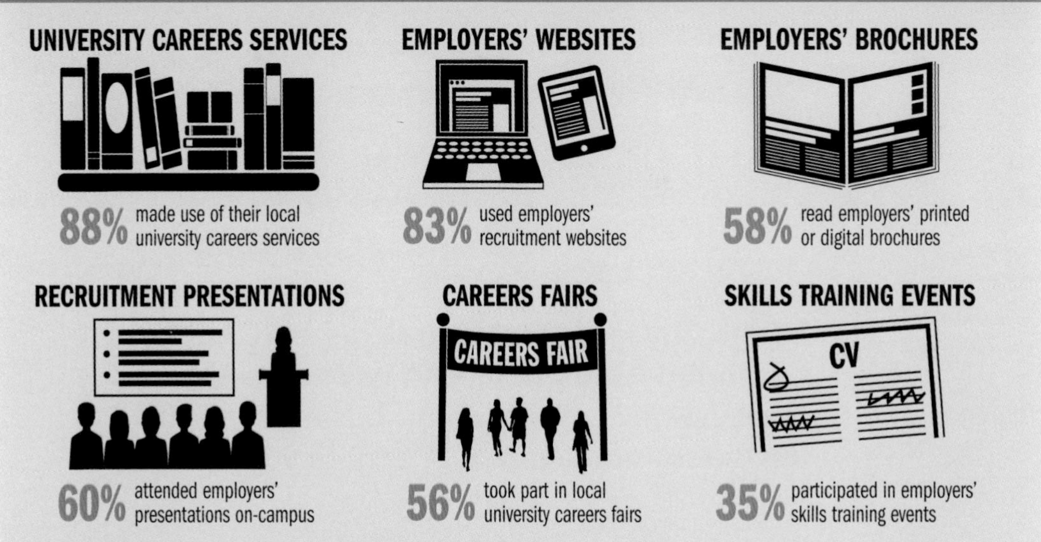

Source **High Fliers Research** 14,271 final year students leaving UK universities in the summer of 2024 were asked which careers resources and information they had used whilst researching graduate employers, during interviews for *The UK Graduate Careers Survey 2024*

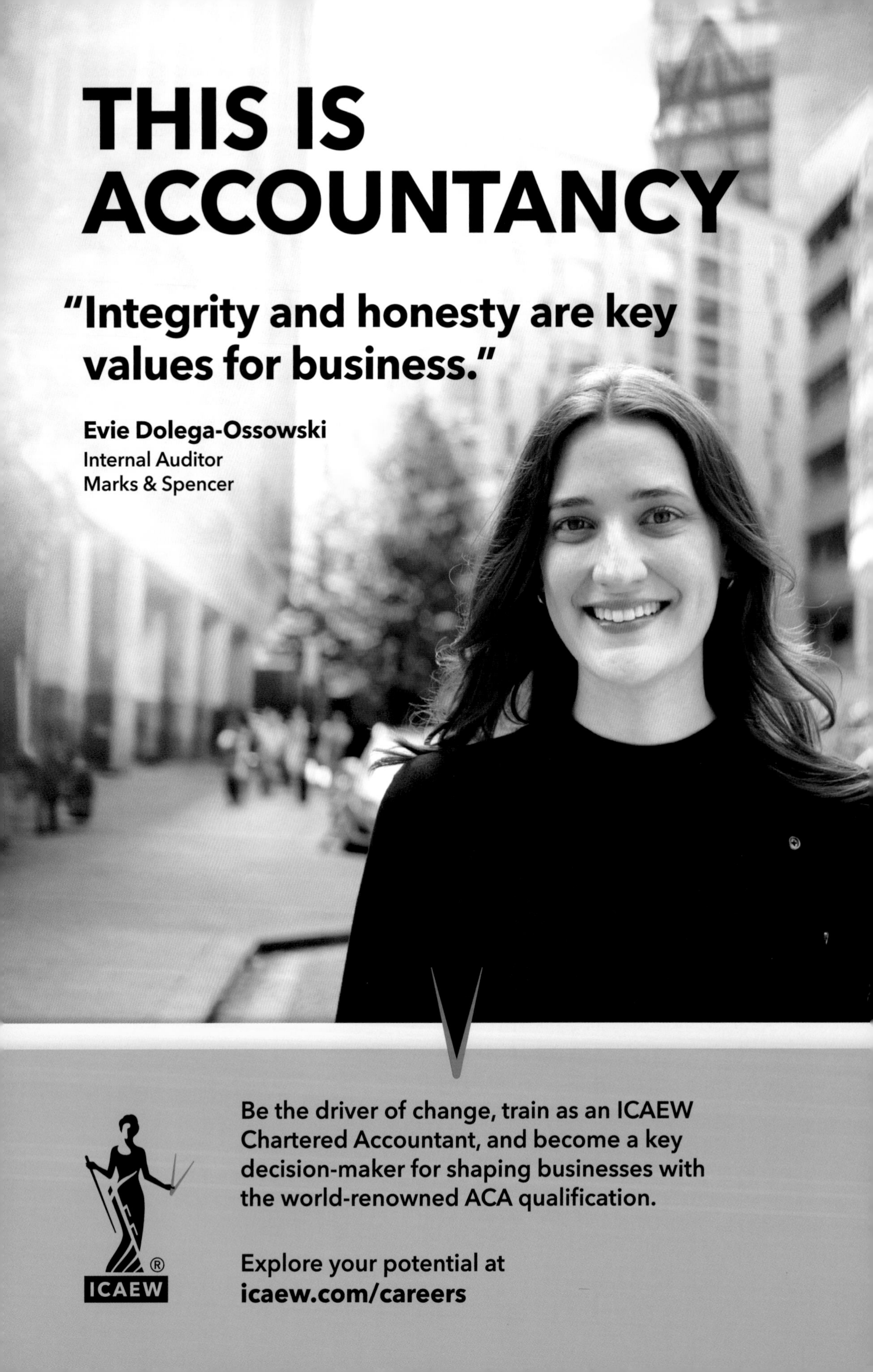
THIS IS ACCOUNTANCY
"Integrity and honesty are key values for business."
Evie Dolega-Ossowski
Internal Auditor
Marks & Spencer
Be the driver of change, train as an ICAEW Chartered Accountant, and become a key decision-maker for shaping businesses with the world-renowned ACA qualification.
Explore your potential at
icaew.com/careers
ICAEW

tips and advice about the application and selection process.

It's important to talk to as many employers as you can – not just those that you are already considering – because the majority of employers who offer entry-level vacancies aren't necessarily household names, nor are they offering graduate jobs that you will be familiar with.

Remember too, as you go round a careers fair, that employers rarely promote 'opportunities for history students', because they are happy to recruit graduates from any degree discipline, provided they have the right skills and can demonstrate they have a real interest in the role they're applying for. This means that almost every employer in the room wants to publicise their programmes to history graduates, along with most other subjects and degree disciplines.

There are several other things that your university careers service can introduce you to in your first year. Online work experience with graduate employers, in either the Christmas, Easter or summer holidays, can be a be a great way to find out about different graduate jobs. And this can fit around doing a part-time local job, if you're using this to fund your university studies.

THE TIMES TOP 100 GRADUATE EMPLOYERS

Start Early for a Career in Banking & Finance

BARCLAYS

Richard Irwin, Global Head of Early Careers, Barclays

"If you're thinking about a graduate job in banking & finance at a global bank like Barclays, then it pays to start preparing as soon as you can.

Around 70 per cent of our graduate intake are students who have done a paid internship at the bank, usually at the end of their second year at university. And up to half of those who do an internship are students who've taken part in one of our first year discovery programmes.

These two-day taster experiences, held at Easter in your first year, give you a proper understanding of what the day-to-day roles are within the bank and introduce you to a network of graduates who are already doing those roles. And during the programme you'll have the chance to be assessed for an internship in your second year too.

To get a place on one of our discovery programmes, you'll need to apply during the autumn of your first year at university. Places are limited and the selection process includes an application form, online assessments that focus on your values, your mindset and your aptitude, and then a final-round assessment day.

We're not expecting you to already have an in-depth knowledge of banking but we are checking if you have the right skills and a real desire to find out more about the opportunities we offer.

If you're applying for one of our 10-week internships in your second year – or a place on our graduate programmes – it is a more competitive process. We would expect you to have a good understanding of the part of the bank you're applying to, by that point. We are very transparent about our assessments and provide plenty of information about what we're assessing at each stage.

To be successful, you need to be able to demonstrate that you've really researched who we are as an employer and that your skillset and values genuinely align with what we're looking for. If you take a scatter-gun approach and make multiple applications to different employers without doing this research, you're much less likely to be offered a place."

Your careers service should have case studies or data on past alumni from your subject or faculty which can be a very helpful starting point if you're trying to work out which types of jobs graduates from your course have gone on to do.

Another way to access alumni could be through a mentoring programme. Many careers services offer students the chance to be mentored through the job-hunting process. Mentors can share their own journey to employment, their personal experiences in the working world, and help you understand whether your skills and outlook would be a good fit for the type of work they're doing.

And don't forget that you may well have careers modules, workshops and external speakers through your university faculty, so keep an eye out for these during your first year too.

For many second year students, the emphasis is often on landing a summer internship or work placement. Your university careers service will offer a varied programme of employer events, discussion panels, networking sessions and skills training that can help you find out which employers are running summer programmes and what it takes to make a successful application.

At this stage, it's helpful to make sure you have an up-to-date CV. Even though most larger employers will want you to complete their own application forms when you apply for internships or a graduate programme, the process of compiling your CV will enable you to draw together much of the information they're looking for. Summarising your academic achievements, the student societies you've been part of, the volunteering or charity work you've done, and your part-time jobs whilst at university, are all elements you'll draw on during the selection process with graduate employers.

When it comes to applying to employers, you may well be tempted to turn to ChatGPT or other AI to help you answer some of the questions on the application form, write a cover letter to accompany your application, or generate practice interview questions. Just remember, for AI to be effective, the information you put in must be personalised and tailored to both your skills and achievements, as well as to what the employer is looking for, otherwise it's not going to work. Watch out too, because some employers do explicitly say they will reject an application if they think you've used AI to complete it.

At its best, AI can generate ideas for you and put structure around your ideas, but it will always need you to edit it, to ensure it reflects your own personal journey and your career plans.

THE TIMES TOP 100 GRADUATE EMPLOYERS

How the 'Class of 2024' Applied for Graduate Jobs

WORK EXPERIENCE

Two-fifths of students who did internships or work placements at university received a **graduate job offer** from the employer they worked for

JOB APPLICATIONS IN FINAL YEAR

Graduates made an average of **16 job applications** each, during their final year at university.

SELECTION & ASSESSMENT

4 out of **5** graduate job hunters found employers' online tests and recorded video interviews **difficult**

GRADUATE JOB OFFERS

Fewer than a **third** of graduates from the 'Class of 2024' received a **graduate job offer** before leaving university

Source **High Fliers Research** 14,271 final year students leaving UK universities in the summer of 2024 were asked about the job applications they had made to graduate employers and their progress with job offers, during interviews for *The UK Graduate Careers Survey 2024*

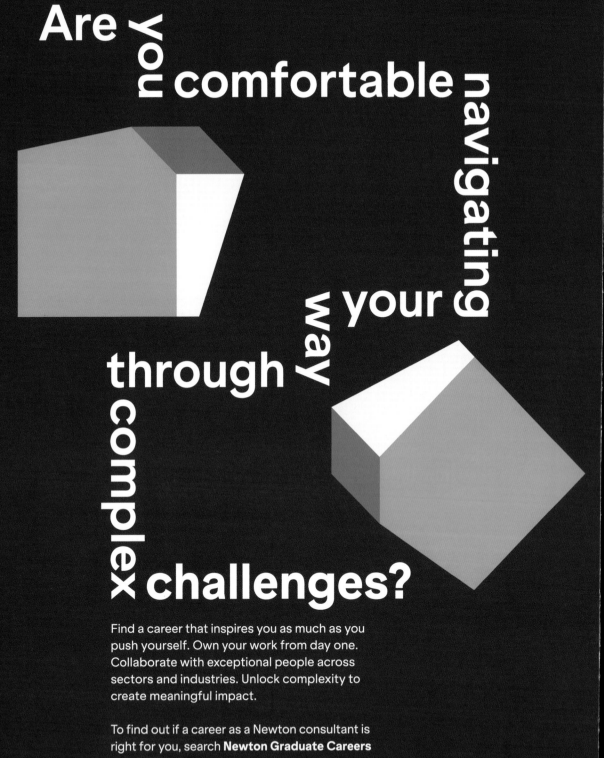
Are you comfortable navigating your way through complex challenges?

But you may find it more helpful to speak to a careers adviser to seek their input on your CV or the applications you're making, particularly if you're not sure how to demonstrate your skills and abilities in an application you're making. It isn't always easy to recognise the experiences you've had and how they might be useful evidence to give to a potential future employer.

Whether you're applying for an internship or making a graduate job application in your final year, the selection process is likely to be very similar. After making the initial application, most employers use online psychometric or aptitude tests and recorded online interviews.

These can seem very difficult and unfamiliar when you first experience them, so it's very important to do as much practice as you can, before you encounter them during an employer's selection process. Your careers service and many individual graduate employers offer workshops and skills sessions, to enable you to try out these tests and master your interview technique. Building up your confidence is an important step towards being successful at this stage.

THE TIMES TOP 100 GRADUATE EMPLOYERS

Embracing the Opportunities in Consulting

"Over the past ten years, consulting has been the number one most-popular destination for new graduates – and in 2024, a record 21 per cent of final year students applied to work as consultants after university.

But what can you expect if you apply for a graduate job in consulting? Capgemini is a global company with over 340,000 employees and clients in more than 50 countries worldwide. In the UK, we recruit around 300 graduates each year to be consultants.

We look for graduates who are passionate about working with clients and bring a variety of strengths, including creativity, collaboration and problem solving. Our consultancy roles are tailor-made for graduates who want to work with world-leading organisations, to support them to become leaders in digital transformation, innovation, customer centricity and sustainability.

Capgemini's graduate programmes last around two years, developing graduates' understanding of consultancy, enriching their soft skills and, where appropriate, focusing on technology and digital skills, including certified training.

Throughout the programme you'll have the opportunity to connect with graduates from across the business, interact with our senior leaders, and hear from a wealth of experts.

One of the biggest attractions of consulting is the variety it brings. Capgemini works across industries such as retail, energy and utilities, healthcare, financial services, telecoms, life sciences, consumer goods, aerospace and defence, manufacturing, and the public sector.

CAPGEMINI

Suzy Style, UK Head of Early Careers Talent Acquisition, Capgemini

Our consultants combine deep knowledge of client industries, with the fast-evolving fields of AI, cloud, connectivity, software, digital engineering, and platforms.

Consulting graduates work as part of a cross-functional team, alongside colleagues who develop and support them as they build up their expertise and knowledge.

You may be part of an assignment that lasts just a few weeks, or it could be a project that is being delivered over a number of years. But we always ensure that our graduates are continually developing and enhancing their skills throughout their careers."

The final selection round for most larger employers is an assessment day or selection centre. These are usually in-person at employers' offices or regional centres and include a number of different exercises and assessments, such as one-to-one interviews, group exercises, presentations and more testing. Again, it's essential to practice each of these elements beforehand, because you don't want your first attempt to be with the employer you most-want to work for.

Completing applications and going through the selection process can be very time-consuming so it's important to be realistic about the number of employers you apply to. On average, employers featured in *The Times Top 100 Graduate Employers* receive between 40 and 50 applications for each graduate vacancy. Or to put that the other way round, they reject 97-98% of the graduate applications they receive.

With such intense competition for places, it's instinctive to try and make a large number of applications, in the hope of improving the odds of landing an offer. But in reality, fewer well-researched, well-written applications will be more successful, especially when coupled with thorough practice and preparation for employers' tests, online interviews and final-round assessments.

If you reach the second half of your final year at university and you haven't received a graduate job offer yet, then the key message is not to panic. Many students do opt to prioritise their academic studies and postpone their graduate job hunting until after graduation. Others choose to take time out or go travelling and up to a fifth of students decide each year to extend their studies with a Masters or other higher-level qualification.

Some employers recruit on a year-round basis and others have multiple intakes during the year, not just September or October start dates, which means you may be able to apply over the summer for a graduate job starting a few months later.

Whichever stage you are at, though, your university careers service will continue to support you preparing applications and getting ready for the selection process, even after you have graduated. And if your initial applications have

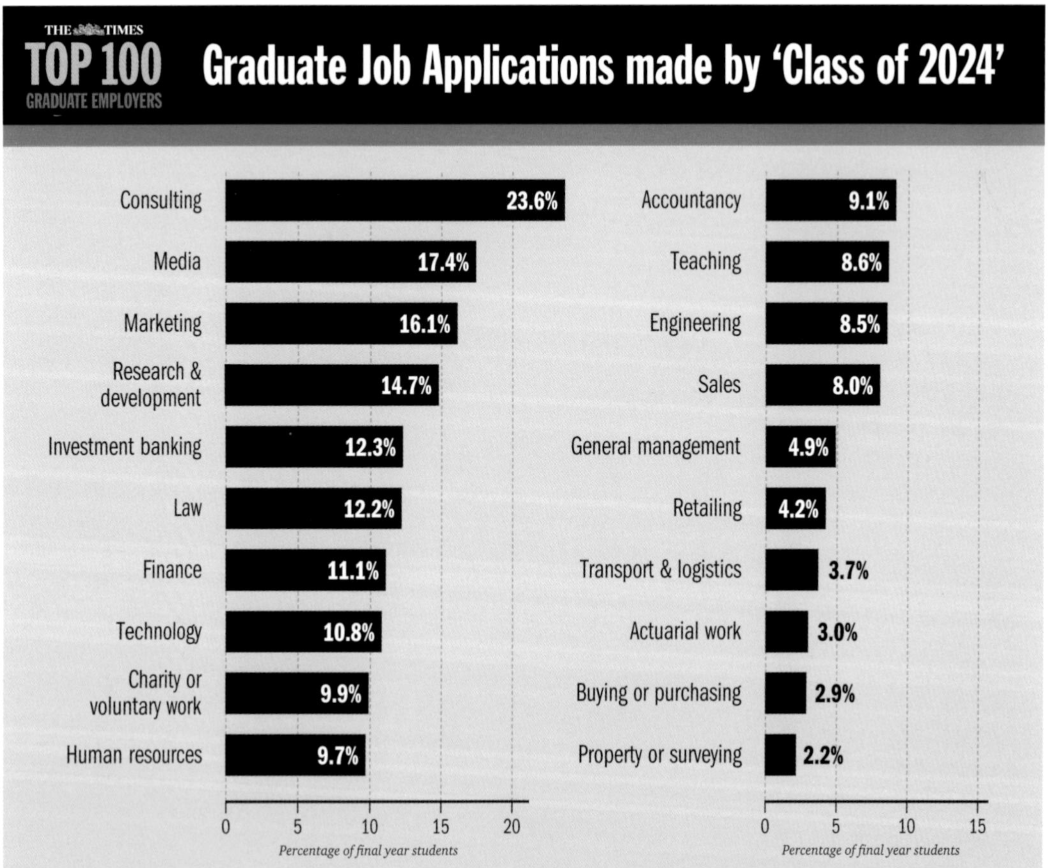

Source **High Fliers Research** 14,271 final year students leaving UK universities in the summer of 2024 were asked about the type of graduate jobs they had applied to or planned to apply to, during interviews for *The UK Graduate Careers Survey 2024*

With ICAS,
opportunity doesn't knock.
It kicks down the door.
Lucy & Chaska
Learn more about how a Chartered Accountancy qualification with ICAS can fast-track your ambitions.
With ICAS, a career in Chartered Accountancy means open access to a whole world of possibilities – so there's no end to where your career could take you.
icas.com/opportunitykicks
icas

proved unsuccessful, they will help you reflect on your career plans and see if there are other opportunities that you may be better suited-to.

Finding your first graduate job can be a very challenging experience but by starting your careers research early, engaging with employers through their work experience programmes, and making use of all the support and resources available through your university, you'll give yourself the very best chance of success.

THE TIMES TOP 100 GRADUATE EMPLOYERS

Applying for a Training Contract at a Top Law Firm

"Slaughter and May is a leading international law firm and we recruit up to 95 graduates each year to train as commercial solicitors.

Trainees are recruited either through our summer work experience programme or by applying directly for a training contract – and we hire a mix of law graduates and those who've studied other subjects at university.

The selection process for a training contract begins with a short application form that asks for your personal and education details, along with your CV and a covering letter. The next stage is to come into the office for an interview, which consists of a written exercise, partner interview and HR interview.

The written exercise is completed on a laptop and is based around a commercial case study, where you're given pieces of information about a fictional business. You'll be asked to review the data and prepare a summary, perhaps as a note to the board of the company, setting out the information, reviewing the options for the business and making a recommendation.

It's really important that lawyers are able to review information and documents they're presented with, analyse it and extract key data, and then write it up in a really clear, concise manner. This exercise is a real-life simulation of the work you'll be doing as a trainee but no prior legal knowledge is needed or expected.

Your partner interview will be with two of the firm's partners – or a partner and a senior legal counsel. Beforehand, you'll be given a recent newspaper article to read along with a set of instructions. It could be business-related or a political piece and you'll have 15 minutes before the interview to summarise the contents, form an opinion on the subject matter, and prepare to have a conversation about it.

The interview itself will last around an hour and will include a discussion about the newspaper article. It's quite a skill to be able to take a lengthy piece, distil it into two or three sentences and then discuss what you conclude from it. This isn't about testing what your opinion is – there is no right or wrong, it's about how you've reached your opinion and the key points you've taken from the original article. Your interviewers may well take an opposing view to yours and challenge you to find out how well thought-out your argument is. It's a test of your ability to think on your feet.

SLAUGHTER AND MAY

Janine Arnold, Head of Recruitment, Slaughter and May

You'll also be asked during the interview about your CV, your degree and your motivation for applying to the firm. It's important to be able to articulate why you want to join Slaughter and May, show you've done your research about the firm and found out why we're different to our competitors. And you'll need to demonstrate you really understand what is involved in a career as a commercial lawyer. "

∫ dx
tpp

THE TIMES

TOP 100
GRADUATE EMPLOYERS

Index

EMPLOYER	RANK	ACCOUNTANCY	CONSULTING	ENGINEERING	FINANCE	GENERAL MANAGEMENT	HUMAN RESOURCES	INVESTMENT BANKING	LAW	LOGISTICS	MARKETING	MEDIA	PROPERTY	PURCHASING	RESEARCH & DEVELOPMENT	RETAIL	SALES	TECHNOLOGY	OTHER	VACANCIES	INSIGHT COURSES	DEGREE PLACEMENTS	SUMMER INTERNSHIPS	PAGE
		GRADUATE VACANCIES IN 2025																			WORK EXPERIENCE			
A&O SHEARMAN	24								●											80-90				56
AECOM	63		●	●									●					●		320		●	●	58
AIRBUS	67			●	●					●				●	●			●		100+		●		60
ALDI	10					●										●				40		●		62
AMAZON	21			●	●	●	●			●										200			●	64
AON	74		●		●													●		120+		●	●	66
ARUP	22		●	●	●					●	●		●		●			●		300		●	●	68
ASTRAZENECA	17			●	●					●	●				●		●			100+		●	●	70
ATKINSRÉALIS	41		●	●																450+	●	●	●	72
BAE SYSTEMS	27	●	●	●	●	●	●				●						●	●		800		●	●	74
BANK OF AMERICA	65	●			●			●										●		No fixed quota	●	●	●	76
BARCLAYS	9			●	●		●	●			●				●		●	●		Around 600	●	●	●	78
BBC	5	●		●	●	●	●		●		●	●			●			●		250+	●		●	80
BCG	32		●																	No fixed quota	●		●	82
BDO	69	●																		Around 800	●	●	●	84
BLACKROCK	37				●		●				●						●	●		170+	●	●	●	86
BLOOMBERG	58			●	●												●	●		350	●	●	●	88
BRITISH AIRWAYS	66			●	●	●				●								●		100	●	●	●	90
CAPGEMINI	95		●	●	●												●	●		300+		●	●	92
CIVIL SERVICE	2	●		●	●		●						●	●	●			●		1,000			●	94
CLYDE & CO	61								●											50	●	●	●	96
DELOITTE	4	●	●		●		●		●				●					●		1,500+	●	●	●	98
DEUTSCHE BANK	96						●	●										●		100+	●	●	●	100
DIAGEO	100			●	●		●				●						●	●		25				102
DLA PIPER	72								●											50+	●		●	104
DYSON	71			●							●				●			●		No fixed quota		●	●	106
ENTERPRISE MOBILITY	59					●										●	●			1,300	●	●	●	108
EY	6	●	●		●				●									●		1,000+	●	●	●	110
FORVIS MAZARS	93	●	●		●													●		400	●	●	●	112
FRESHFIELDS	45								●											Up to 100	●		●	114
GOOGLE	8		●	●			●				●						●	●		No fixed quota			●	116
GRANT THORNTON	98	●	●		●															350-400		●	●	118
GSK	20			●	●	●				●	●			●	●		●			25+		●	●	120
HOGAN LOVELLS	82								●											50	●		●	122

EMPLOYER	RANK	ACCOUNTANCY	CONSULTING	ENGINEERING	FINANCE	GENERAL MANAGEMENT	HUMAN RESOURCES	INVESTMENT BANKING	LAW	LOGISTICS	MARKETING	MEDIA	PROPERTY	PURCHASING	RESEARCH & DEVELOPMENT	RETAIL	SALES	TECHNOLOGY	OTHER	VACANCIES	INSIGHT COURSES	DEGREE PLACEMENTS	SUMMER INTERNSHIPS	PAGE
		GRADUATE VACANCIES IN 2025																			WORK EXPERIENCE			
HSBC	13				●	●		●										●		600+	●	●	●	124
IBM	35		●															●		150+				126
UK INTELLIGENCE SERVICES	55/86			●	●	●	●											●	●	500+	●		●	128
ITV	46	●			●	●	●		●		●	●			●		●	●		No fixed quota	●	●	●	130
J.P. MORGAN	7	●			●		●								●		●	●		400+	●	●	●	132
KPMG	11	●	●						●									●		1,000		●	●	134
L'ORÉAL	19				●		●			●	●			●			●			40-50	●	●	●	136
LATHAM & WATKINS	62								●											32	●	●	●	138
LIDL	48					●				●				●		●				30-50				140
LINKLATERS	31								●											100	●		●	142
LLOYDS BANKING GROUP	12	●		●	●		●	●										●		100+	●	●	●	144
M&S	64					●								●		●				60+				146
MICROSOFT	44		●								●						●	●		No fixed quota		●		148
MOTT MACDONALD	83		●	●																400		●	●	150
NATWEST GROUP	29		●		●	●	●				●							●		250	●	●	●	152
NESTLÉ	90			●			●			●	●				●		●			25-35		●		154
NEWTON	28		●																	Around 100			●	156
NHS	3	●			●	●	●											●		200	●	●	●	158
P&G	26			●	●		●			●	●				●		●	●		100		●	●	160
PENGUIN	36	●			●		●				●	●			●	●	●	●		250	●		●	162
PFIZER	40			●	●	●					●							●		15-20		●	●	164
POLICE NOW	33																		●	400				166
PWC	1	●	●		●				●									●		1,500+	●	●	●	168
ROLLS-ROYCE	25			●		●												●		No fixed quota		●	●	170
ROYAL AIR FORCE	81			●		●	●		●	●								●		500+				172
ROYAL NAVY	39			●	●	●	●		●	●		●			●			●		No fixed quota	●	●	●	174
SANTANDER	73				●	●		●								●		●		75			●	176
SAVILLS	97			●									●							130+	●	●	●	178
SLAUGHTER AND MAY	49								●											95	●		●	180
TEACH FIRST	15																		●	1,750	●			182
TRANSPORT FOR LONDON	84			●	●	●	●					●	●	●				●		50+	●		●	184
UNLOCKED	51																		●	143				186
WHITE & CASE	57								●											50	●		●	188
WSP	70		●	●	●								●							180+		●	●	190

- You'll receive **one-to-one support** from an adviser with years of classroom experience. They'll guide you through the steps and answer any questions you may have.
- With **generous bursaries and scholarships** available across certain subjects, including STEM, you'll get advice on how to fund your training year.
- You'll find out how to get a taste of life in the classroom, from school experience days to paid internships.
- You'll learn about the career progression teaching offers, with a **starting salary of £30k** (or more in London) and the opportunity to earn **over £41k within five years.**

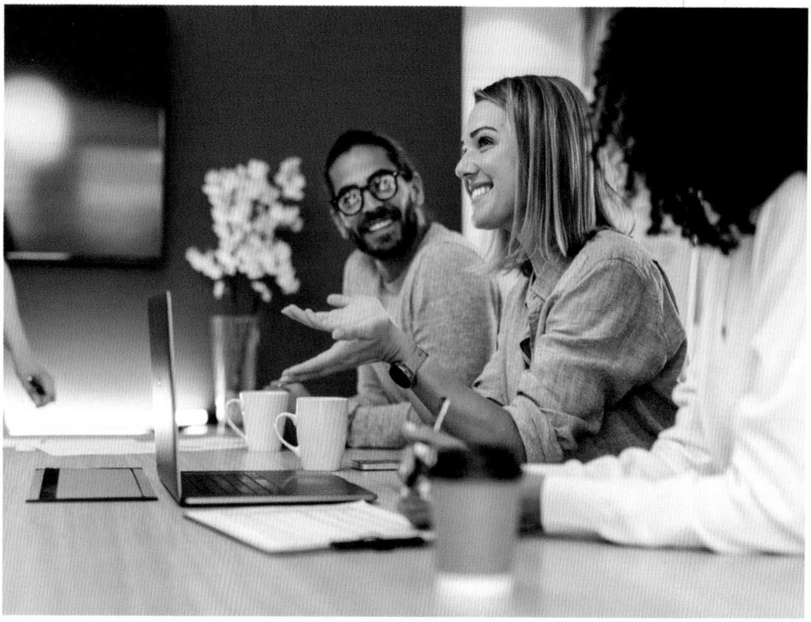

Since the two legal powerhouses – Allen & Overy and Shearman & Sterling – joined forces in May 2024, A&O Shearman has proven to be an unparalleled combination: a new type of industry leader with truly global capabilities, helping the world's leading businesses to grow, innovate, and thrive.

In today's ever-changing world, A&O Shearman continue to break new ground, working with companies, organisations and governments on the most complex legal issues and building strong and enduring client relationships. With offices in a vast range of global locations, graduates will work on the most interesting, high-profile legal work.

The A&O Shearman training contract is characterised by flexibility and choice. It is meticulously designed and continually evolving to provide the foundations trainees need to find their strengths, overcome challenges and bring out their best self. It's a chance to really discover life as a lawyer. Training will be based on four six-month rotations (known as 'seats'), through a number of departments or practice areas. The seat structure ensures that all trainees see as many parts of the firm as possible and that learning is hands-on and guided by a senior associate or partner. Trainees could also spend a seat on an international or client secondment and gain contentious experience, either by spending a seat in the firm's litigation department, or by completing a litigation course and obtaining experience via legal advice clinics.

A&O Shearman offers vacation scheme opportunities to students and graduates from all degree disciplines. Each year they have two schemes across winter and summer. These are designed to show students exactly what it's like to tackle exciting challenges every day and experience global success as part of A&O Shearman's friendly, supportive, and dynamic culture.

GRADUATE VACANCIES IN 2025

LAW

NUMBER OF VACANCIES

80-90 graduate jobs

For training contracts starting in 2027.

LOCATIONS OF VACANCIES

Vacancies also available in Europe, the USA, Asia and elsewhere in the world.

STARTING SALARY FOR 2025

£56,000

Rising to £61,000 in year two and £150,000 for NQ.

UNIVERSITY PROMOTIONS DURING 2024-2025

BIRMINGHAM, BRISTOL, CAMBRIDGE, DURHAM, EXETER, GLASGOW, KENT, LANCASTER, LEEDS, LEICESTER, MANCHESTER, NOTTINGHAM, OXFORD, WARWICK, YORK

Please check with your university careers service for full details of A&O Shearman's local promotions and events.

MINIMUM ENTRY REQUIREMENTS

2.1 Degree,
136 UCAS points

APPLICATION DEADLINE

Please see website for full details.

FURTHER INFORMATION

www.Top100GraduateEmployers.com

*Register now for the latest news, local promotions, work experience and graduate vacancies at **A&O Shearman**.*

aecom.com/uk-ireland-graduate-careers

@AECOM aecomgraduaterecruitment@aecom.onmicrosoft.com

AecomTechnologyCorporation linkedin.com/company/aecom

@AECOM youtube.com/AECOMTechnologyCorp

AECOM

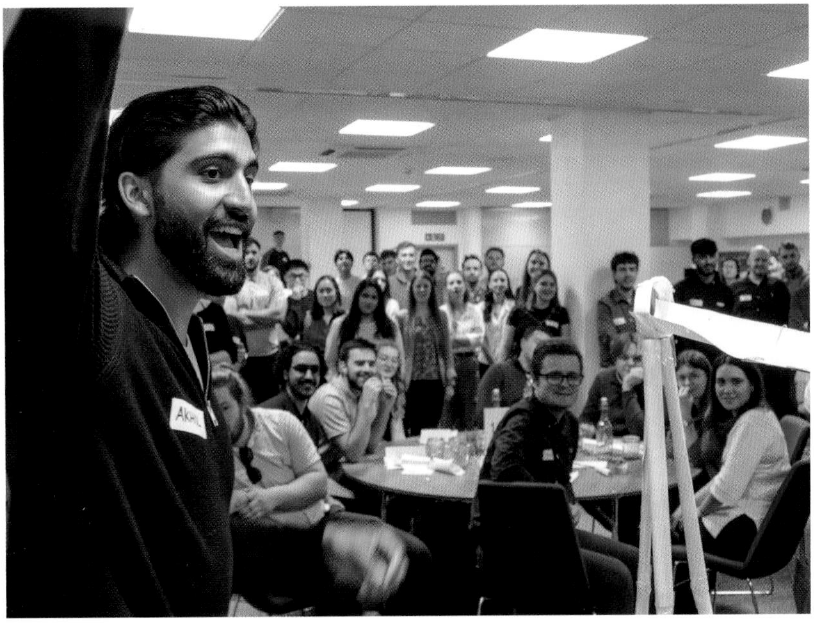

AECOM believe infrastructure creates opportunity for everyone – uplifting communities, improving access and sustaining the planet. They are trusted engineers, consultants, designers, planners, and more – delivering professional services spanning cities, transportation, buildings, water, energy, and environment.

AECOM are committed to managing their business with the upmost responsibility and always strive for better – be that reducing emissions, creating social value or diversifying their senior leadership and workforce. As part of the firm, graduates make a tangible impact on communities and the environment. AECOM have opportunities in building engineering, bridges, roads, rail, water, energy, surveying, project management, planning, architecture, environment – such as ecology, air quality, carbon capture, acoustics, and much more.

AECOM offers up to 150 undergraduate summer and industrial placements in all parts of the business and across all offices. These range from 6-weeks to 12-months and provide students with the opportunity to develop their technical skills and industry knowledge, experience the culture, and demonstrate their skills and attributes which may then lead to a permanent graduate role upon graduation.

All of AECOM's graduates complete the ADVANCE programme designed to help build their career at the firm. It includes instructor-led training sessions where they meet their peers and senior leadership, career development, wellbeing, project delivery, bidding, presentation skills and projects in action, to equip them with the knowledge and skills needed to succeed.

The programme also includes an online curriculum via AECOM University, webinars, networking opportunities, and full support towards accreditation with the relevant professional institution.

GRADUATE VACANCIES IN 2025

- CONSULTING
- ENGINEERING
- PROPERTY
- TECHNOLOGY

NUMBER OF VACANCIES

320 graduate jobs

LOCATIONS OF VACANCIES

Vacancies also available in Europe, the USA, Asia and elsewhere in the world.

STARTING SALARY FOR 2025

£28,500-£31,500

WORK EXPERIENCE

DEGREE PLACEMENTS | SUMMER INTERNSHIPS

UNIVERSITY PROMOTIONS DURING 2024-2025

ASTON, BATH, BIRMINGHAM, BRISTOL, CAMBRIDGE, CARDIFF, COVENTRY, DURHAM, EDINBURGH, EXETER, GLASGOW, HERIOT-WATT, IMPERIAL COLLEGE LONDON, LEEDS, LIVERPOOL, LIVERPOOL JOHN MOORES, LOUGHBOROUGH, MANCHESTER, NEWCASTLE, NORTHUMBRIA, NOTTINGHAM, NOTTINGHAM TRENT, OXFORD BROOKES, PLYMOUTH, PORTSMOUTH, QUEEN'S UNIVERSITY, BELFAST, READING, SHEFFIELD, SOUTHAMPTON, SURREY, ULSTER, UNIVERSITY COLLEGE LONDON, WARWICK, WEST OF ENGLAND (UWE)

MINIMUM ENTRY REQUIREMENTS

2.1 Degree

APPLICATION DEADLINE

Year-round recruitment

FURTHER INFORMATION

www.Top100GraduateEmployers.com

Register now for the latest news, local promotions, work experience and graduate vacancies at ***AECOM.***

AECOM
Help lead the change towards a sustainable and equitable future
Architecture and Interior Design
Building Engineering and Sustainability
Design, Planning and Economics
Energy
Environmental Consulting
Geotechnical and Tunnelling Engineering
Landscape Architecture
Surveying and Project Management
Transportation Engineering and Planning
Water Engineering and Consulting
2024
THE TIMES
TOP 50
EMPLOYERS
FOR GENDER
EQUALITY
Find out how you can make an impact
aecom.com/uk/impact
Delivering a better world

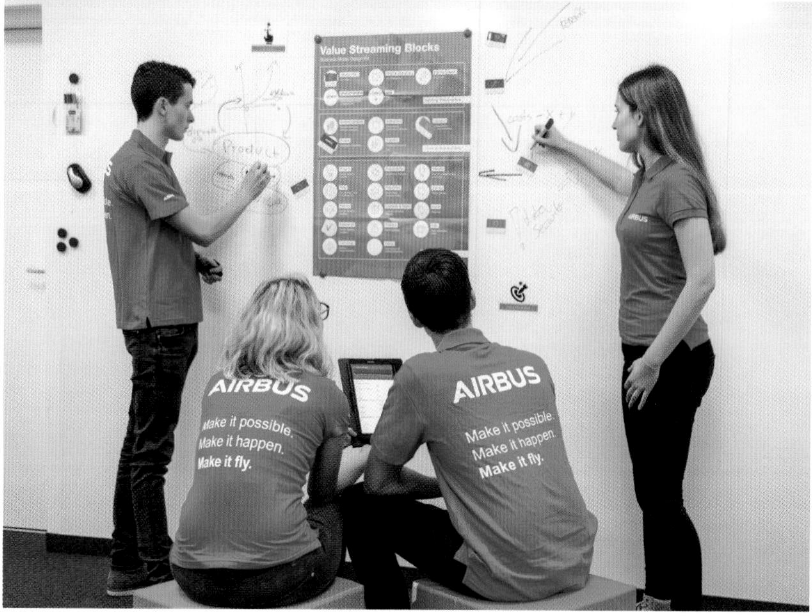

Airbus is a pioneer in aerospace with a team of more than 140,000 people in 180 locations worldwide working on the design, manufacture, and maintenance of commercial aircraft, as well as satellites, space technology, secure communication systems, and helicopters for customers across the world.

Every year, Airbus looks for people with the ambition, enthusiasm, and talent to help them pioneer sustainable aerospace for a safe and united world. Students and recent graduates can apply to join Airbus' graduate programmes across the company's businesses with teams in engineering, finance, marketing, communications, procurement, cyber, and many more. New graduates will be based at one of five sites in the UK, or at one of Airbus' sites in Europe, Asia, or the Americas. The Airbus Global Graduate Programme (AGGP) sees graduates joining teams around the world on a development pathway that will assist their growth into skilled positions.

Airbus offers more than 100 12-month placement experiences each year at several of their UK sites. Placements are across all departments and a multitude of functions. Students are immersed in their team's activities, given high levels of responsibility, and supported to deliver projects impacting Airbus' products and teams both locally and around the world.

At Airbus graduates are given opportunities to develop their technical and soft skills as part of the graduate programme. In addition, everyone at Airbus has access to thousands of online training solutions for use at any time.

Graduates work in several teams during the programme to help with a broad understanding of the company. For example, they may join the engineering programme, but spend time with the finance, manufacturing, or public affairs team, depending on individual development needs.

GRADUATE VACANCIES IN 2025
- ENGINEERING
- FINANCE
- LOGISTICS
- PURCHASING
- RESEARCH & DEVELOPMENT
- TECHNOLOGY

NUMBER OF VACANCIES
100+ graduate jobs

LOCATIONS OF VACANCIES

Vacancies also available in Europe, the USA, Asia and elsewhere in the world.

STARTING SALARY FOR 2025
£31,000
Plus profit sharing, relocation, and employee share plans.

WORK EXPERIENCE
DEGREE PLACEMENTS

UNIVERSITY PROMOTIONS DURING 2024-2025
BATH, BRISTOL, CARDIFF, EXETER, IMPERIAL COLLEGE LONDON, LANCASTER, LEEDS, LIVERPOOL, LIVERPOOL JOHN MOORES, MANCHESTER, NOTTINGHAM, READING, SHEFFIELD, SHEFFIELD HALLAM, WEST OF ENGLAND (UWE)
Please check with your university careers service for full details of Airbus' local promotions and events.

MINIMUM ENTRY REQUIREMENTS
Relevant degree required for some roles.

APPLICATION DEADLINE
20th October 2024

FURTHER INFORMATION
www.Top100GraduateEmployers.com
*Register now for the latest news, local promotions, work experience and graduate vacancies at **Airbus**.*

Discover
your future
with us
A321 AIRBUS
scan me if you can!
A321XLR
Apply now
airbus.com/careers
#AirbusCareers
AIRBUS

ALDI

graduate@aldi.co.uk

AldiCareersUK linkedin.com/company/aldi-uk

@AldiEarlyCareersUK @AldiCareersUK

Arriving in the UK back in 1990, Aldi is now the UK's fourth largest supermarket, with over 1,010 stores and 45,000 colleagues – and don't forget about their global presence. It's a business with integrity – everything Aldi does is for the benefit of customers, colleagues and the community.

Third year students or recent graduates can apply for Aldi's Area Manager Programme, renowned for the £50,000 starting salary and incredible level of responsibility. Through the support of a dedicated training programme and network of experienced colleagues, graduates will become responsible for a portfolio of stores within their first 12 months. They will shadow an experienced area manager mentor and take charge of their own area for a short period, overseeing the rota, ordering products, and managing store teams.

Area managers will get to know the accounts, trading, warehouse & transport and business administration teams, equipping them with a 360-degree view of the business. As personnel leader to their store teams, area managers coach and lead their teams to success. Supporting over 100 colleagues within their area, the ability to motivate and drive their teams is essential. As the first training year draws to a close, graduates will take on their own designated group of stores and hit the ground running for a lifelong rewarding career.

For penultimate year students, Aldi offer 12-month long placements. The Retail Management Placement offers a pathway to the Area Manager Programme. Students will spend six months in store, shadowing the store manager and area manager, learning what it takes to run a successful store. Students will then move into an office-based environment and take on a national project. Aldi also offer several exciting opportunities across IT, HR, supply chain management, buying, customer interaction and real estate, at their head office in Atherstone.

GRADUATE VACANCIES IN 2025

GENERAL MANAGEMENT

RETAIL

NUMBER OF VACANCIES

40 graduate jobs

LOCATIONS OF VACANCIES

STARTING SALARY FOR 2025

£50,000

WORK EXPERIENCE

DEGREE PLACEMENTS

UNIVERSITY PROMOTIONS DURING 2024-2025

ABERDEEN, ABERYSTWYTH, ASTON, BANGOR, BATH, BIRMINGHAM, BRADFORD, BRISTOL, BRUNEL, CAMBRIDGE, CARDIFF, CITY, DUNDEE, DURHAM, EDINBURGH, ESSEX, EXETER, GLASGOW, HERIOT-WATT, HULL, IMPERIAL COLLEGE LONDON, KENT, LANCASTER, LEEDS, LEICESTER, LIVERPOOL, LOUGHBOROUGH, MANCHESTER, NEWCASTLE, NORTHUMBRIA, NOTTINGHAM, NOTTINGHAM TRENT, OXFORD, OXFORD BROOKES, PLYMOUTH, QUEEN MARY LONDON, READING, ROYAL HOLLOWAY LONDON, SHEFFIELD, SOUTHAMPTON, ST ANDREWS, STIRLING, STRATHCLYDE, SURREY, SUSSEX, SWANSEA, UEA, ULSTER, UNIVERSITY COLLEGE LONDON, WARWICK, YORK

MINIMUM ENTRY REQUIREMENTS

2.1 Degree

APPLICATION DEADLINE

Year-round recruitment

FURTHER INFORMATION

www.Top100GraduateEmployers.com

*Register now for the latest news, local promotions, work experience and graduate vacancies at **Aldi**.*

amazon

amazon.jobs

@Amazon AmazonUK

@AmazonOpsLife linkedin.com/company/amazon

Amazon's mission is to be Earth's most customer-centric company. This is what unites Amazonians across teams and geographies as they all strive to delight customers and make their lives easier, one innovative product, service, and idea at a time.

Every year, Amazon offers hundreds of graduates the opportunity to design their path to a successful career. From day one, graduates are given leadership positions with significant responsibilities. Amazon believes in hiring and developing the best, which is why graduates are given numerous opportunities to acquire technical skills that will enable them to take on future projects and careers within the company.

Amazon encourages graduates to have a self-starter mentality when it comes to learning, and they supplement this with hands-on training to enable their people to progress and succeed. There are opportunities across a broad range of teams within engineering, technology, research, and business, and many graduates join the organisation as Area Managers, leading and developing teams. Amazon is looking for people who are ready to dedicate their time and energy, fuelled by their passion.

Amazon is a company of builders who bring diverse backgrounds, ideas, and points of view to inventing on behalf of their customers. This diversity comes from many sources, including gender, race, age, national origin, sexual orientation, culture, education, and professional and life experience. Amazon is committed to diversity and inclusion, and they are always looking for ways to scale their impact as they grow. Their internships and full-time roles for graduates give new joiners the opportunity to solve problems, innovate on behalf of customers, and shape the business.

GRADUATE VACANCIES IN 2025

- ENGINEERING
- FINANCE
- GENERAL MANAGEMENT
- HUMAN RESOURCES
- LOGISTICS

NUMBER OF VACANCIES

200 graduate jobs

LOCATIONS OF VACANCIES

Vacancies also available in Europe.

STARTING SALARY FOR 2025

£31,000-£37,000

Plus relocation allowance, sign-on and RSU bonuses.

WORK EXPERIENCE

INTERNSHIPS

UNIVERSITY PROMOTIONS DURING 2024-2025

ASTON, BATH, BIRMINGHAM, BRISTOL, CAMBRIDGE, CARDIFF, CITY, DURHAM, EDINBURGH, EXETER, GLASGOW, IMPERIAL COLLEGE LONDON, KING'S COLLEGE LONDON, LANCASTER, LEEDS, LEICESTER, LIVERPOOL, LONDON SCHOOL OF ECONOMICS, LOUGHBOROUGH, MANCHESTER, NEWCASTLE, NOTTINGHAM, OXFORD, QUEEN MARY LONDON, READING, SHEFFIELD, SOUTHAMPTON, ST ANDREWS, STRATHCLYDE, SWANSEA, UNIVERSITY COLLEGE LONDON, WARWICK, YORK

APPLICATION DEADLINE

Year-round recruitment

FURTHER INFORMATION

www.Top100GraduateEmployers.com

Register now for the latest news, local promotions, work experience and graduate vacancies at ***Amazon.***

every day better

AON

aon.com/careers/uk

Aonplc · graduates@aon.co.uk
@Aon_plc · linkedin.com/company/aon
@lifeataon · youtube.com/AonCorporation

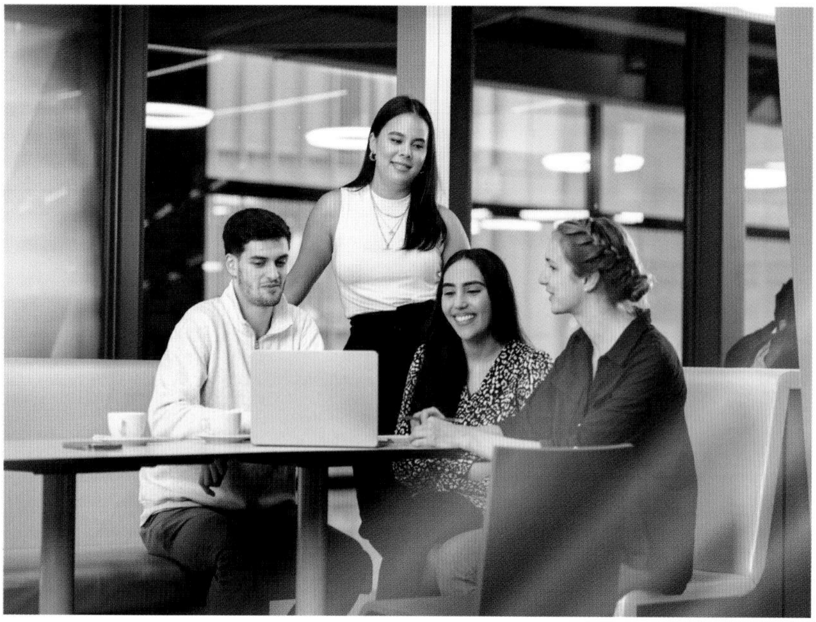

As a leading global professional services firm, Aon exists to shape decisions for the better, to protect and enrich the lives of people around the world. Aon provide their clients in over 120 countries with the clarity and confidence to make better risk and people decisions that help protect and grow their businesses.

Aon believes that businesses thrive when the communities they serve and the people they employ also flourish. At Aon, their people are the heartbeat of the firm. They have a passion for bringing the best to their clients, which unites them and drives them as a global firm.

Graduates and undergraduates can join Aon across a range of consulting and broking roles within business areas including actuarial analysis, investment, insurance, reinsurance, and catastrophe modelling.

Launch, Aon's graduate development programme, is designed to help graduates develop their technical expertise, business knowledge, professional skills and qualifications, and provide them with opportunities to grow their career. As participants on the programme, successful graduates will apply their analytical capabilities, commercial awareness, and interpersonal skills to help clients address the key questions that affect their businesses. How will the rise of inflation and cost of living affect the ability to conduct business and bring goods to the people who need them? What could climate change mean to Europe? Aon's business is to provide the answers to help clients make better decisions.

Aon believe diverse and inclusive teams create better insights and solutions, deliver the best outcomes for clients, and most importantly, are a vital part of ensuring long-term success. Aon stands united to foster an environment where all are welcomed.

GRADUATE VACANCIES IN 2025

CONSULTING
FINANCE
TECHNOLOGY

NUMBER OF VACANCIES

120+ graduate jobs

LOCATIONS OF VACANCIES

STARTING SALARY FOR 2025

£Competitive

WORK EXPERIENCE

DEGREE PLACEMENTS | SUMMER INTERNSHIPS

UNIVERSITY PROMOTIONS DURING 2024-2025

BATH, BIRMINGHAM, BRISTOL, CAMBRIDGE, DURHAM, EXETER, GLASGOW, HERIOT-WATT, IMPERIAL COLLEGE LONDON, KENT, LEEDS, MANCHESTER, NOTTINGHAM, WARWICK

Please check with your university careers service for full details of Aon's local promotions and events.

MINIMUM ENTRY REQUIREMENTS

2.1 Degree

APPLICATION DEADLINE

Please see website for full details.

FURTHER INFORMATION

www.Top100GraduateEmployers.com

Register now for the latest news, local promotions, work experience and graduate vacancies at ***Aon.***

Sasa - Aon Graduate

ARUP

careers.arup.com/earlycareers

UKEarlyCareersRecruitment@arup.com
ArupGroup linkedin.com/company/arup
@arupuk @arupgroup youtube.com/arupgroup

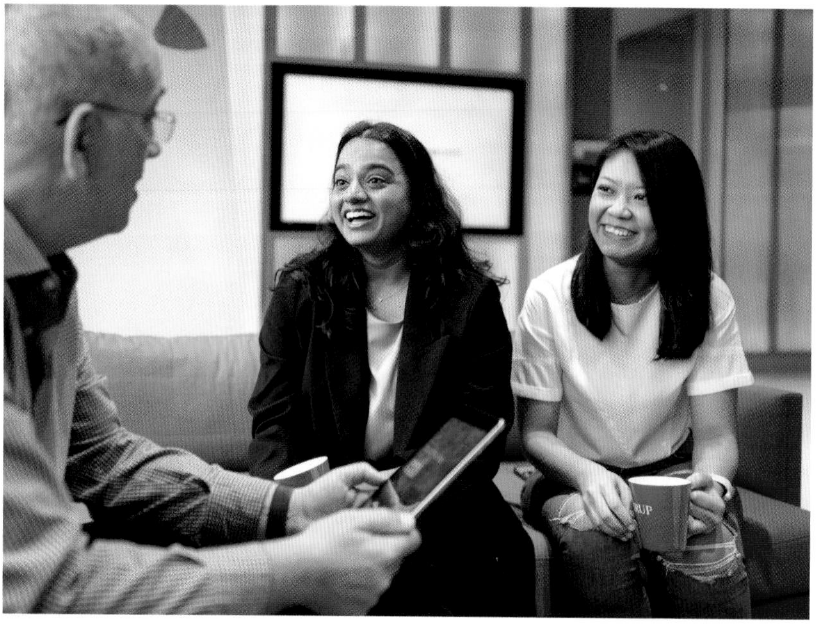

Dedicated to sustainable development, Arup is a collective of designers, consultants and experts working globally. Founded to be humane and excellent, they collaborate with their clients and partners using imagination, technology, and rigour to shape a better world.

At Arup, graduates have real autonomy to work on projects and engage with clients from the start. They gain a breadth of experience by working on interesting projects that strengthen the resilience of communities and places to improve lives, and create a lasting impact on the world. In return, Arup expect graduates to push boundaries, challenge and improve how they do things, and to remain curious about the evolving world around them.

Whatever field of study, there are a wide range of opportunities on offer across the UK with roles in: energy, water & resources, climate & sustainability, advisory, building services & building performance, structural & civil engineering, transport & ground engineering, planning, and digital services, to name a few.

Graduates are encouraged to pursue a professional qualification of their choice with the support of a designated mentor. Arup partners with many professional institutes such as ICE, IStructE, IMechE, IET, CIBSE, RICS, so graduates can choose a path that suits them. On top of this, they will benefit from a fantastic training package which includes access to the Skills Networks, hundreds of courses available at Arup University (their in-house training team), and informal networking.

Whether looking for a temporary summer role, a longer placement of up to 12 months, or a graduate position, Arup offer many possibilities that will suit all career aspirations. Join them and build a future with purpose.

GRADUATE VACANCIES IN 2025

- CONSULTING
- ENGINEERING
- FINANCE
- LOGISTICS
- MARKETING
- PROPERTY
- RESEARCH & DEVELOPMENT
- TECHNOLOGY

NUMBER OF VACANCIES

300 graduate jobs

LOCATIONS OF VACANCIES

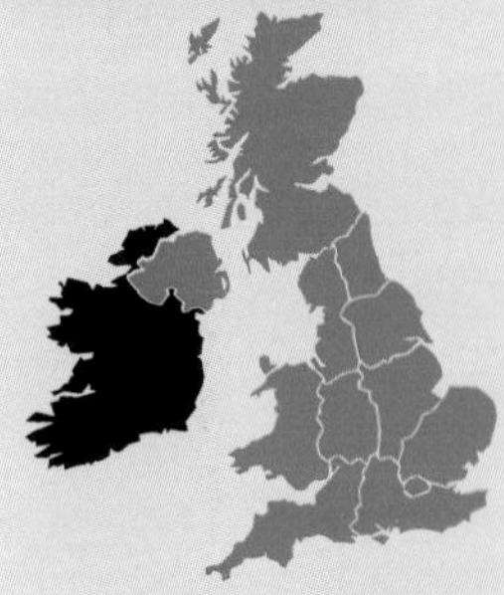

STARTING SALARY FOR 2025

£30,200

Plus a £2,500 bonus.

WORK EXPERIENCE

DEGREE PLACEMENTS | SUMMER INTERNSHIPS

UNIVERSITY PROMOTIONS DURING 2024-2025

Please check with your university careers service for full details of Arup's local promotions and events.

MINIMUM ENTRY REQUIREMENTS

2.1 Degree

Relevant degree required for some roles.

APPLICATION DEADLINE

Please see website for full details.

FURTHER INFORMATION

www.Top100GraduateEmployers.com

Register now for the latest news, local promotions, work experience and graduate vacancies at Arup.

AstraZeneca

careers.astrazeneca.com/early-talent

@AstraZeneca AstraZeneca
linkedin.com/company/astrazeneca
@AstraZeneca youtube.com/astrazeneca

AstraZeneca is a global, science-led, patient-focused pharmaceutical company employing 100,000 people worldwide. They are dedicated to transforming the future of healthcare by unlocking the power of what science can do for people, society and the planet.

AstraZeneca's graduate programmes, which are open to bachelor's and master's level applicants, offer a wide variety of learning opportunities and potential for growth. With career paths spanning the medical life cycle, graduates could join AstraZeneca in areas such as clinical development, data science and AI, finance, manufacturing, or supply.

Graduates are empowered to jump in, take the initiative, be part of meaningful project teams, and make an impact by delivering real value to patients and the business. The programmes place an emphasis on personal and professional development, investing in each graduate's unique interests and potential. Projects will be tailored to the individual and their future ambitions.

Operating in a fast-paced, yet deeply supportive and collaborative environment, graduates are encouraged to take responsibility and apply their knowledge in practical settings. AstraZeneca's graduates work hard, building a rich and supportive network that will last a lifetime. They will have significant opportunities to build bonds with their international peers, developing connections and growing their network with experts and leaders across the business.

The programmes bring diverse talent from all over the world together to gain an international perspective and combine strengths and knowledge to multiply impact. AstraZeneca is proud of its award-winning, progressive working practices. The company welcomes diverse thinking, curiosity, collaboration and the courage to go further, together.

GRADUATE VACANCIES IN 2025

- ENGINEERING
- FINANCE
- LOGISTICS
- MARKETING
- RESEARCH & DEVELOPMENT
- SALES

NUMBER OF VACANCIES

100+ graduate jobs

LOCATIONS OF VACANCIES

STARTING SALARY FOR 2025

£32,500

Plus benefits fund, bonus and relocation (if applicable).

WORK EXPERIENCE

DEGREE PLACEMENTS | SUMMER INTERNSHIPS

UNIVERSITY PROMOTIONS DURING 2024-2025

ASTON, BATH, BIRMINGHAM, BRISTOL, BRUNEL, CAMBRIDGE, CARDIFF, EXETER, GLASGOW, IMPERIAL COLLEGE LONDON, KENT, KING'S COLLEGE LONDON, LANCASTER, LEEDS, LEICESTER, LIVERPOOL, LSE, MANCHESTER, NEWCASTLE, OXFORD, QUEEN MARY LONDON, SHEFFIELD, SOAS LONDON, SOUTHAMPTON, SUSSEX, UNIVERSITY COLLEGE LONDON, WARWICK, YORK

Please check with your university careers service for full details of AstraZeneca's local promotions and events.

APPLICATION DEADLINE

Please see website for full details.

FURTHER INFORMATION

www.Top100GraduateEmployers.com

*Register now for the latest news, local promotions, work experience and graduate vacancies at **AstraZeneca**.*

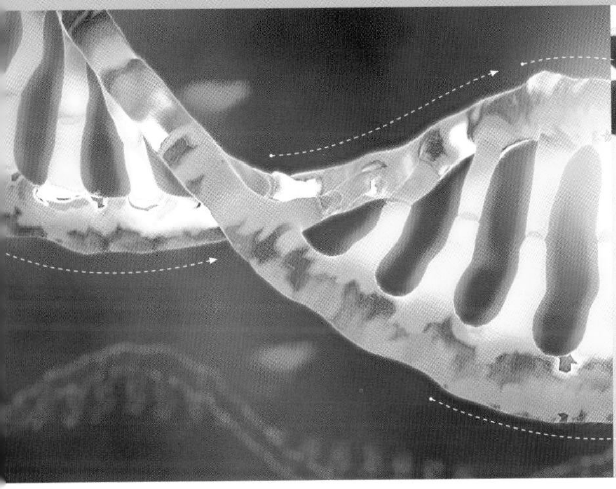

careers.atkinsrealis.com/uk-early-careers

AtkinsRéalis

InsideAtkins · linkedin.com/company/atkinsrealis

@inside_atkinsrealis · youtube.com/@atkinsrealisglobal

AtkinsRéalis is a world-class engineering services and nuclear organisation. They work with clients on local, national and international projects across sectors including transportation, infrastructure, environment, water, energy, defence, technology, and aerospace.

AtkinsRéalis offer a wide range of two-year graduate development programmes nationally across engineering, technical and non-technical disciplines. Roles typically include: environmental, project management, civil and structural engineering, ground engineering and tunnelling, mechanical engineering, electrical engineering, human factors, transport planning, digital and technology, nuclear fusion, software, management consulting, rail consulting, data intelligence, chemical and process engineering, along with opportunities in airport planning and surveying.

The graduate development programme features a series of training events and modules, professional development, mentoring and on-the-job experience, to help graduates gain the skills and knowledge they need to develop their career and work towards professional qualifications. Graduates join AtkinsRéalis from a wide range of disciplines including engineering, digital and technology, the sciences, mathematics, geography/GIS, project management, business studies, law, humanities, chemistry, data/computer science, and many more.

AtkinsRéalis offer two types of placements: 8-week summer schemes and 12-month industrial placements. Both are full-time paid work posts, designed to support and complement the academic learning of undergraduate and postgraduate students who are studying a relevant degree. On joining, graduates enjoy an induction and settling-in buddy scheme to familiarise themselves with the organisation. They also join a vibrant, sociable early careers community.

GRADUATE VACANCIES IN 2025

CONSULTING

ENGINEERING

NUMBER OF VACANCIES

450+ graduate jobs

LOCATIONS OF VACANCIES

STARTING SALARY FOR 2025

£29,000-£32,750

Plus a £2,500 settling in payment.

WORK EXPERIENCE

INSIGHT COURSES | DEGREE PLACEMENTS | SUMMER INTERNSHIPS

UNIVERSITY PROMOTIONS DURING 2024-2025

BATH, BIRMINGHAM, BRISTOL, CARDIFF, DERBY, DURHAM, IMPERIAL COLLEGE LONDON, LEEDS, LIVERPOOL JOHN MOORES, LOUGHBOROUGH, MANCHESTER, NOTTINGHAM, NOTTINGHAM TRENT, SHEFFIELD, SOUTHAMPTON, STRATHCLYDE, SURREY, SWANSEA, UNIVERSITY COLLEGE LONDON, WARWICK

Please check with your university careers service for full details of AtkinsRéalis' local promotions and events.

MINIMUM ENTRY REQUIREMENTS

2.2 Degree

APPLICATION DEADLINE

December 2024 - April 2025

FURTHER INFORMATION

www.Top100GraduateEmployers.com

*Register now for the latest news, local promotions, work experience and graduate vacancies at **AtkinsRéalis**.*

BAE SYSTEMS

@LifeBAESystems | LifeatBAESystems | @LifeatBAESystems | linkedin.com/company/bae-systems

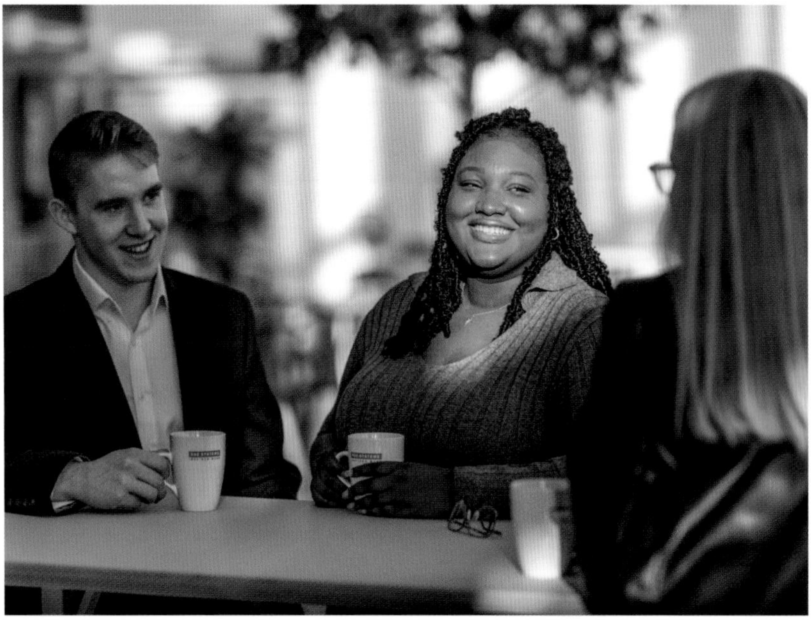

BAE Systems provide some of the world's most advanced, technology-led defence, aerospace and security solutions. They develop, engineer, manufacture, and support products and systems to protect national security and people, and keep critical information and infrastructure secure.

Graduates joining BAE Systems will join a purpose that binds almost 100,000 diverse minds and talents together – to serve, supply and protect. They will work on projects across air, land, sea, cyber and space as part of a premier international defence, aerospace and security company. With opportunities available nationwide, graduate programmes develop skills of the future in engineering, technology or business and are non-rotational with varying durations and structures.

With over 50 sites across the UK, BAE Systems' graduate programmes give students a solid platform to build and launch their career, with exposure to live projects and real responsibilities. Graduates will be provided with all the training and support they need to achieve their ambitions. It's a flexible, inclusive and collaborative culture where everyone has the chance to build a varied career and is empowered to achieve their goals.

BAE Systems offers 12-month industrial placements, 12-week summer internships and insight experiences, allowing undergraduates to gain valuable skills and experience to take back to their studies, and secure their future.

At every stage of their career, first-class training, coaching and development programmes, role models and mentors will help BAE Systems graduates embrace their potential. Working on real projects, with real responsibilities, collaborating with the brightest minds, and exploring what life is really like at BAE Systems – all whilst earning a competitive salary.

GRADUATE VACANCIES IN 2025

- ACCOUNTANCY
- CONSULTING
- ENGINEERING
- FINANCE
- GENERAL MANAGEMENT
- HUMAN RESOURCES
- MARKETING
- SALES
- TECHNOLOGY

NUMBER OF VACANCIES

800 graduate jobs

LOCATIONS OF VACANCIES

STARTING SALARY FOR 2025

£34,000

Plus a £2,000 starting bonus.

WORK EXPERIENCE

DEGREE PLACEMENTS | SUMMER INTERNSHIPS

UNIVERSITY PROMOTIONS DURING 2024-2025

ABERDEEN, ASTON, BATH, BIRMINGHAM, BOURNEMOUTH, BRISTOL, CAMBRIDGE, CARDIFF, CENTRAL LANCASHIRE, CRANFIELD, DUNDEE, DURHAM, EDINBURGH, EXETER, GLASGOW, IMPERIAL COLLEGE LONDON, KENT, KING'S COLLEGE LONDON, LANCASTER, LEEDS, LEICESTER, LIVERPOOL JOHN MOORES, LIVERPOOL, LOUGHBOROUGH, MANCHESTER, NEWCASTLE, NOTTINGHAM TRENT, NOTTINGHAM, OXFORD, PLYMOUTH, PORTSMOUTH, QUEEN MARY LONDON, ROYAL HOLLOWAY LONDON, SHEFFIELD, SOUTHAMPTON, STRATHCLYDE, SURREY, UNIVERSITY COLLEGE LONDON, WARWICK, YORK

MINIMUM ENTRY REQUIREMENTS

2.2 Degree

Relevant degree required for some roles.

APPLICATION DEADLINE

Year-round recruitment

FURTHER INFORMATION

www.Top100GraduateEmployers.com

*Register now for the latest news, local promotions, work experience and graduate vacancies at **BAE Systems**.*

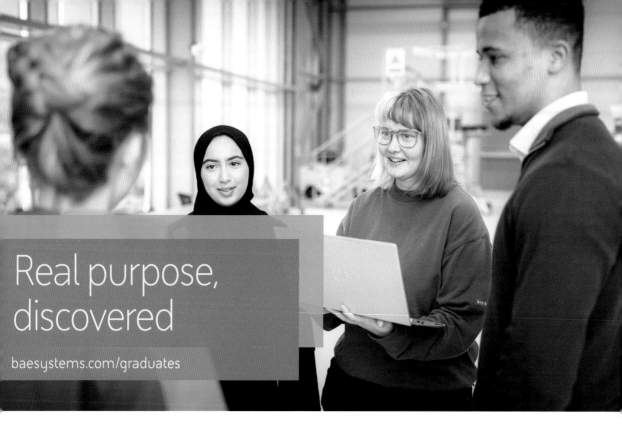

campus.bankofamerica.com

@BankofAmerica juniortalentemea@bofa.com

linkedin.com/company/bank-of-america-business

@BankofAmerica youtube.com/bankofamerica

BANK OF AMERICA

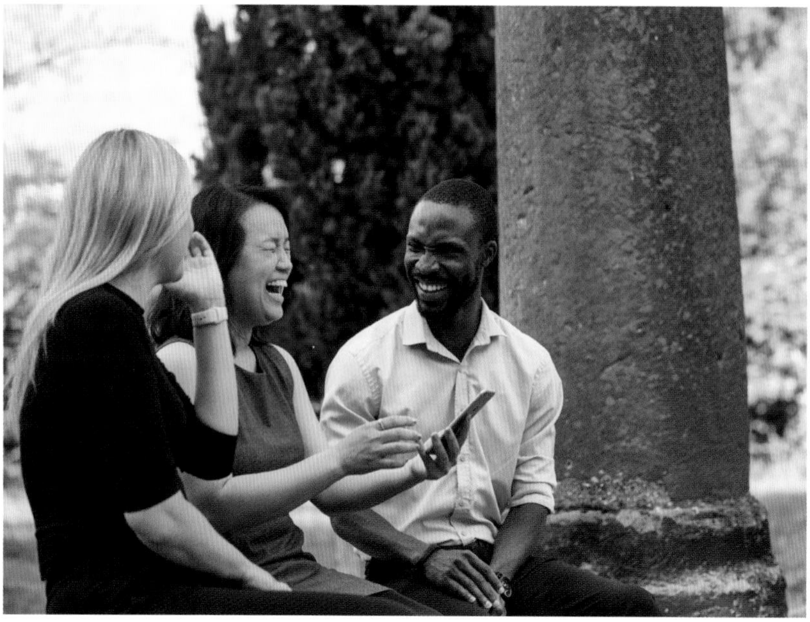

Bank of America is one of the world's leading financial institutions, serving individuals, small and middle-market businesses, large corporations, and governments with a full range of banking, investment management and other financial and risk management products and services.

Bank of America welcomes graduates from all universities, degrees and backgrounds into its diverse and inclusive workplace. They firmly believe all employees should be treated with respect and be able to bring their whole selves to work. This is core to who they are as a company and how they drive responsible growth. Bank of America offers a range of early careers programmes, including apprenticeships, insight courses, internships, industrial placements and full time Analyst and Associate graduate programmes.

Graduates can join Bank of America in areas including Audit, Research, Risk, Sales & Trading, Technology and more. Each line of business offers unique opportunities, and there's plenty of collaboration across the bank designed to shape a smarter, greener, safer and more inclusive world. This includes everything from helping clients achieve sustainable growth, and working with external partners to increase the number of women working in tech.

All programmes offer formal, ongoing training and development opportunities, structured performance evaluations, mentoring support and networking opportunities. As well as getting involved in exciting client projects, graduates are encouraged to make the most of the various internal groups and events such as sport and social club activities, employee network events and volunteering programmes. All of these opportunities give teammates the chance to shape a meaningful career, build connections both within and outside the bank and spend time on what matters to them.

GRADUATE VACANCIES IN 2025

- ACCOUNTANCY
- FINANCE
- INVESTMENT BANKING
- TECHNOLOGY

NUMBER OF VACANCIES

No fixed quota

LOCATIONS OF VACANCIES

Vacancies also available in Europe.

STARTING SALARY FOR 2025

£Competitive

WORK EXPERIENCE

INSIGHT COURSES | DEGREE PLACEMENTS | SUMMER INTERNSHIPS

UNIVERSITY PROMOTIONS DURING 2024-2025

BANGOR, BATH, BIRMINGHAM, BRISTOL, CAMBRIDGE, DURHAM, EDINBURGH, IMPERIAL COLLEGE LONDON, KING'S COLLEGE LONDON, LANCASTER, LEEDS, LIVERPOOL, LONDON SCHOOL OF ECONOMICS, MANCHESTER, NOTTINGHAM, OXFORD, QUEEN MARY LONDON, SOUTHAMPTON, SURREY, UNIVERSITY COLLEGE LONDON, WARWICK, YORK

Please check with your university careers service for full details of Bank of America's local promotions and events.

MINIMUM ENTRY REQUIREMENTS

2.1 Degree

APPLICATION DEADLINE

25th October 2024

Recruiting on a rolling basis so early application is advised.

FURTHER INFORMATION

www.Top100GraduateEmployers.com

*Register now for the latest news, local promotions, work experience and graduate vacancies at **Bank of America**.*

Barclays are a global, vital and highly respected financial organisation with an inspiring purpose. Operating in 39 countries with around 100,000 people across the world, they help communities, individuals and businesses thrive. And, they've created financial solutions and technology that the world now takes for granted.

Joining Barclays as a graduate or intern means the opportunity to do truly meaningful work, to discover a financial company that's focused on a better future for everyone, and to develop skills that will pave the way for a career that's both challenging and inspiring. Spanning everything from technology to investment banking, Barclays' two global graduate programmes will either develop graduates into a technical expert in their chosen field or help to build an extraordinary depth and breadth of experience through a deep dive into a chosen business area. Meanwhile, interns at the bank are immersed in real projects with real outcomes.

At Barclays, graduates and interns help to shape the future. The bank has a legacy of innovation, from introducing the first ATMs to launching contactless payments. Today, that forward-thinking approach continues. Barclays is committed to being a net zero bank by 2050, for example, and is experimenting with emerging technologies like blockchain and quantum computing.

Those joining can expect immediate responsibility, exciting collaborations, and ongoing training. This means Barclays looks for graduates with an innate sense of curiosity, along with the agility and adaptability it takes to come up with new ideas that can become ground-breaking.

With an inclusive culture, Barclays welcomes people from all walks of life. They empower their employees to always be themselves, finding their place in their community of individuals. Making a difference, by being different. This is what it feels like to start a career at Barclays.

GRADUATE VACANCIES IN 2025

- ENGINEERING
- FINANCE
- HUMAN RESOURCES
- INVESTMENT BANKING
- MARKETING
- RESEARCH & DEVELOPMENT
- SALES
- TECHNOLOGY

NUMBER OF VACANCIES

Around 600 graduate jobs

LOCATIONS OF VACANCIES

STARTING SALARY FOR 2025

£Competitive

Graduates receive scholarship and bursary payments.

WORK EXPERIENCE

INSIGHT COURSES | DEGREE PLACEMENTS | SUMMER INTERNSHIPS

UNIVERSITY PROMOTIONS DURING 2024-2025

ABERDEEN, ASTON, BIRMINGHAM, BIRMINGHAM CITY, CAMBRIDGE, CENTRAL LANCASHIRE, DUNDEE, DURHAM, EDGE HILL, EDINBURGH, EXETER, GLASGOW, GLASGOW CALEDONIAN, GREENWICH, IMPERIAL COLLEGE LONDON, LIVERPOOL, LIVERPOOL HOPE, LOUGHBOROUGH, LSE, MANCHESTER, MANCHESTER METROPOLITAN, NORTHAMPTON, NOTTINGHAM, OXFORD, ST ANDREWS, STRATHCLYDE, UNIVERSITY COLLEGE LONDON, UNIVERSITY OF THE WEST OF SCOTLAND, WARWICK, WOLVERHAMPTON

APPLICATION DEADLINE

Please see website for full details.

FURTHER INFORMATION

www.Top100GraduateEmployers.com

Register now for the latest news, local promotions, work experience and graduate vacancies at ***Barclays.***

BBC

bbc.co.uk/earlycareers

@BBCGetIn earlycareersrecruitment@bbc.co.uk
@lifeatthebbc linkedin.com/company/bbc

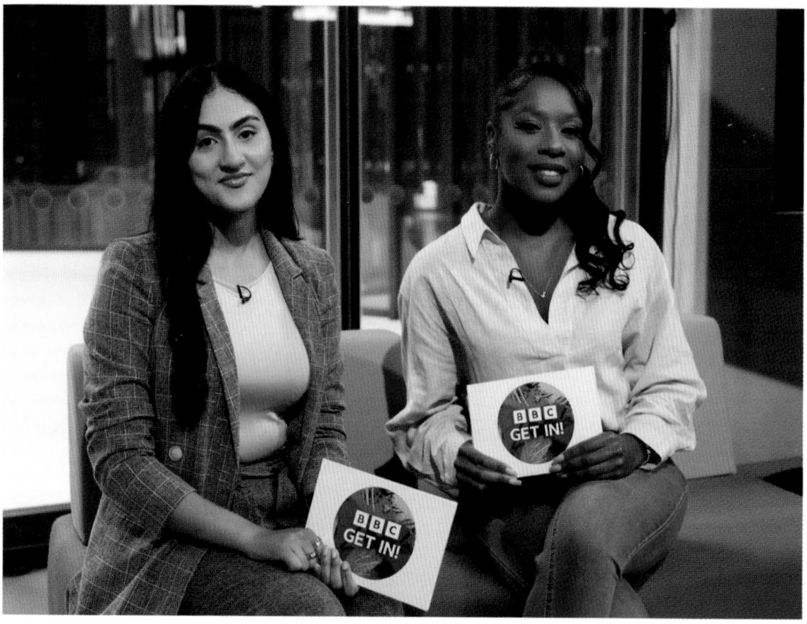

The BBC is the world's leading public service broadcaster, producing distinctive, world-class programmes and content which inform, educate, and entertain millions of people in the UK and around the world. More than 18,000 staff work at the BBC in journalism, production, engineering, technology, and business.

The BBC delivers content through a portfolio of television services, national and local radio networks, BBC World Service and a range of digital services. With a strong focus on potential rather than the level of academic achievement, the BBC has school leaver, graduate, postgraduate-level and career changer apprenticeship schemes in journalism, engineering, software engineering, research and development, UX design, marketing, business and law.

BBC schemes include a mix of on-the-job learning and academic study, giving successful applicants the opportunity to gain a formal qualification. Different perspectives are important to the BBC, as is motivation for the role, a positive attitude and an appetite for curiosity.

Evidence of good communication skills, team working and creativity will strengthen applications. Successful applicants will receive a dedicated team manager and scheme specialist to help with their development, professional teaching and mentoring by industry experts, and access to industry-leading training through the BBC Academy.

The BBC's apprenticeship schemes for 2025 are expected to open for applications in Autumn 2024, with assessment centres taking place in early 2025 for a September start. The BBC is committed to skills and talent development, and as one of the world's most creative and technologically-advanced organisations for the last 100 years, a career at the BBC means learning from the best.

GRADUATE VACANCIES IN 2025

- ACCOUNTANCY
- ENGINEERING
- FINANCE
- GENERAL MANAGEMENT
- HUMAN RESOURCES
- LAW
- MARKETING
- MEDIA
- RESEARCH & DEVELOPMENT
- TECHNOLOGY

NUMBER OF VACANCIES
250+ graduate jobs

LOCATIONS OF VACANCIES

STARTING SALARY FOR 2025
£21,840-£32,500

WORK EXPERIENCE
INSIGHT COURSES | SUMMER INTERNSHIPS

UNIVERSITY PROMOTIONS DURING 2024-2025
Please check with your university careers service for full details of BBC's local promotions and events.

APPLICATION DEADLINE
November 2024 - January 2025

FURTHER INFORMATION
www.Top100GraduateEmployers.com
*Register now for the latest news, local promotions, work experience and graduate vacancies at **BBC**.*

BCG

careers.bcg.com

@BCGinUK linkedin.com/company/boston-consulting-group

When organisations find problems they can't solve on their own, that's where BCG gets to work. As the pioneer in business strategy consulting, it has been helping to solve some of the world's biggest problems since it was founded nearly 60 years ago. Today, its work is more fascinating than ever.

Graduates will join a 32,000-strong global team of consultants and subject-matter experts to partner with global clients on projects that make positive change happen. BCG helps organisations flourish in a world where sustainability is the priority. To date, BCG has delivered almost £2 billion's worth of consulting projects focused on social impact, and has made its own pledge to achieve net-zero climate impact by 2030.

Working at BCG, graduates will start making an impact on day one, with early exposure to the most senior leaders of global corporations. There are opportunities to build experience across different industries and sectors, and to work in projects at the forefront of technology, like advanced robotics, artificial intelligence, and blockchain.

This focus on the future means that BCG offers unparalleled opportunities for growth and development. The firm never stops learning: it continually invests in its employees with in-depth learning experiences, curated and led by senior BCG members and top-tier trainers from around the world.

BCG looks for bright students from any subject matter or discipline. It values people with high academic achievement, leadership skills, deep intellectual curiosity, and a problem-solving mindset. Diversity of thought, expertise, experience, and background are fundamental to BCG's success. For graduates looking to continue their learning journey and make a real difference in the world, BCG is the place to start.

GRADUATE VACANCIES IN 2025

CONSULTING

NUMBER OF VACANCIES

No fixed quota

LOCATIONS OF VACANCIES

STARTING SALARY FOR 2025

£Competitive

Competitive compensation and benefits package including an annual discretionary performance related bonus.

WORK EXPERIENCE

INSIGHT COURSES | SUMMER INTERNSHIPS

UNIVERSITY PROMOTIONS DURING 2024-2025

BATH, BIRMINGHAM, BRISTOL, CAMBRIDGE, CARDIFF, DURHAM, EDINBURGH, EXETER, GLASGOW, IMPERIAL COLLEGE LONDON, KING'S COLLEGE LONDON, LEEDS, LIVERPOOL, LONDON SCHOOL OF ECONOMICS, MANCHESTER, NEWCASTLE, NOTTINGHAM, OXFORD, SCHOOL OF AFRICAN STUDIES, SHEFFIELD, SOUTHAMPTON, ST ANDREWS, UNIVERSITY COLLEGE LONDON, WARWICK, YORK

MINIMUM ENTRY REQUIREMENTS

2.1 Degree

APPLICATION DEADLINE

24th October 2024

FURTHER INFORMATION

www.Top100GraduateEmployers.com

Register now for the latest news, local promotions, work experience and graduate vacancies at BCG.

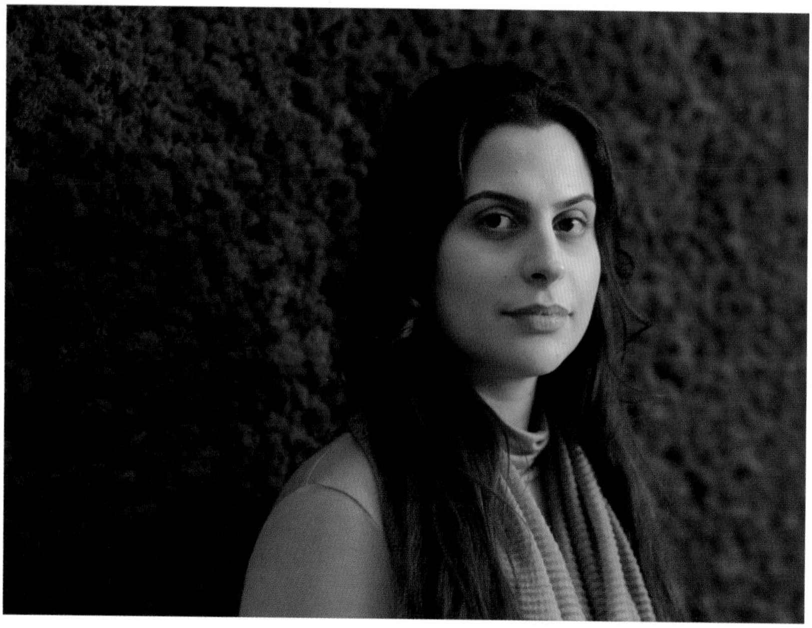

Accountancy and business advisory firm, BDO employs over 8,000 people across 18 offices in the UK, providing the solutions ambitious and entrepreneurial businesses need to navigate today's changing world. BDO UK is part of the BDO global network, providing advisory services in 166 countries.

When the most innovative and high-growth businesses need advice on accountancy and business, they turn to BDO. With expertise across financial services, healthcare, leisure and hospitality, retail, manufacturing, technology, media, not-for-profit, public sector and many more industries, BDO provides the advice and answers that help AIM listed companies achieve their aspirations. Specialising in tax, audit & assurance and advisory, BDO's graduate programmes are for those who want to work with ambitious clients on challenging work from day one.

BDO look for trainees who want to bring themselves to everything they do. Those who are prepared to ask questions, offer up ideas and seize every opportunity. Those who have a drive to inspire more conversations and build lasting relationships. In return, BDO will provide a breadth of experience and opportunities to develop skills that few could match.

The three-year graduate programme will see trainees combine a real job with paid study leave to work towards professional qualifications like the ACA, CFA and CTA, to become an expert in a chosen area. At BDO, trainees are shaped into the independent and ethical advisors the UK's most forward-thinking businesses rely on. With early exposure to clients, trainees experience varied work that will broaden their horizons. The firm provides expert coaching and mentoring at every step, so that trainees can build a career with confidence.

Go beyond the ordinary, with a career at BDO.

GRADUATE VACANCIES IN 2025

ACCOUNTANCY

NUMBER OF VACANCIES

Around 800 graduate jobs

LOCATIONS OF VACANCIES

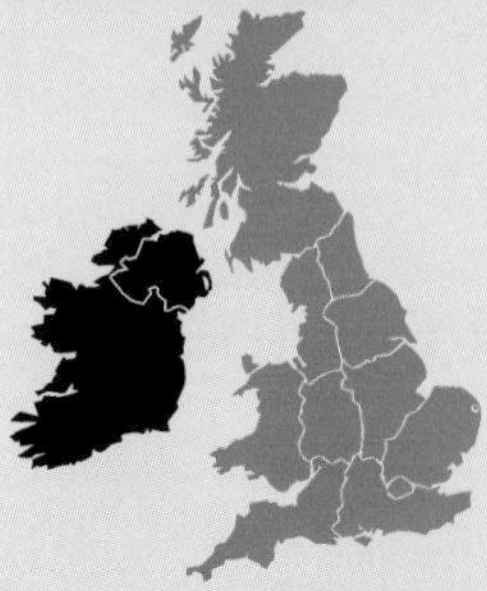

STARTING SALARY FOR 2025

£26,000-£32,000

Varies by region and role.

WORK EXPERIENCE

INSIGHT COURSES | DEGREE PLACEMENTS | SUMMER INTERNSHIPS

UNIVERSITY PROMOTIONS DURING 2025-2025

ANGLIA RUSKIN, ASTON, BATH, BIRMINGHAM, BIRMINGHAM CITY, BRIGHTON, BRISTOL, CARDIFF, COVENTRY, DE MONTFORT, DURHAM, EDINBURGH, ESSEX, EXETER, GLASGOW, GLASGOW CALEDONIAN, HERIOT-WATT, KING'S COLLEGE LONDON, LEEDS, LEICESTER, LIVERPOOL, LIVERPOOL JOHN MOORES, LOUGHBOROUGH, MANCHESTER, MANCHESTER METROPOLITAN, NEWCASTLE, NOTTINGHAM, NOTTINGHAM TRENT, PORTSMOUTH, QUEEN MARY LONDON, READING, SHEFFIELD, SOUTHAMPTON, STRATHCLYDE, SUFFOLK, SURREY, SUSSEX, UEA, UNIVERSITY COLLEGE LONDON, WARWICK, YORK

APPLICATION DEADLINE

Programmes will open for applications in September 2024. Early application is advised.

FURTHER INFORMATION

www.Top100GraduateEmployers.com

*Register now for the latest news, local promotions, work experience and graduate vacancies at **BDO**.*

BlackRock

careers.blackrock.com/early-careers

@BlackRock (X) linkedin.com/company/blackrock
@BlackRock (Instagram) youtube.com/blackrock

BlackRock is a global investment management company that helps individuals and institutions achieve their financial goals. BlackRock offers a range of products and services, such as mutual funds, ETFs, portfolio management, risk analysis, and advisory solutions.

BlackRock offers a range of graduate programmes tailored for students eager to begin their careers in fintech. These programmes cater to various interests and skill sets, including asset management, technology, analytics and business operations. Open to graduates from all academic backgrounds, BlackRock provides opportunities in several business areas, including client & product, corporate & strategic, investments, technology, and operations. The specific tasks and responsibilities vary based on the role and team they join, but students can anticipate engaging in meaningful work, collaborating with colleagues and clients, and contributing to BlackRock's mission to forge a better financial future for all.

BlackRock is set to offer a variety of internships and work experience programmes in 2025, including an 8-week summer internship, spring insight event and 3-12 month placements.

BlackRock is dedicated to offering graduates unparalleled training and development opportunities to foster their growth and success in their careers. Graduates at BlackRock can expect: A comprehensive training programme that encompasses both technical and soft skills, along with industry knowledge and insights. Graduates will benefit from on-the-job coaching, feedback, and support from their managers and team, as well as access to a wealth of online learning resources and courses. They will join a diverse and inclusive community that encourages collaboration, while embarking on a clear and transparent career path that facilitates their progression within the firm.

GRADUATE VACANCIES IN 2025
- FINANCE
- HUMAN RESOURCES
- MARKETING
- SALES
- TECHNOLOGY

NUMBER OF VACANCIES
170+ graduate jobs

LOCATIONS OF VACANCIES

Vacancies also available in Europe.

STARTING SALARY FOR 2025
£Competitive
Plus a sign-on bonus.

WORK EXPERIENCE
INSIGHT COURSES | DEGREE PLACEMENTS | SUMMER INTERNSHIPS

UNIVERSITY PROMOTIONS DURING 2024-2025
EDINBURGH NAPIER
Please check with your university careers service for full details of BlackRock's local promotions and events.

APPLICATION DEADLINE
27th September 2024 - 25th October 2024

FURTHER INFORMATION
www.Top100GraduateEmployers.com
Register now for the latest news, local promotions, work experience and graduate vacancies at ***BlackRock.***

Bloomberg

bloomberg.com/company/what-we-do

emea_recruit@bloomberg.net
Bloomberg | linkedin.com/company/bloomberg
@BloombergBusiness | youtube.com/insidebloomberg

As a global information and technology company, Bloomberg uses its dynamic network of data, ideas and analysis to solve difficult problems every day. Its customers around the world rely on them to deliver accurate, real-time business and market information that helps them make important financial decisions.

Bloomberg is guided by four core values: innovation, collaboration, customer service, and doing the right thing. The European Headquarters in London is a testament to that innovation, as it is the world's most sustainable office building.

Bloomberg offers insight weeks, internship and full-time entry-level roles at their London office across a range of business areas including Analytics & Sales, Data, Engineering, Operations and more. Candidates who join Bloomberg can build and define their own unique career, rather than a pre-defined path.

Bloomberg is proud to have a truly global dynamic organisation, so all employees are empowered to have an impact and are measured by their contributions. All graduate starters will participate in team-specific training that continues throughout their career via robust career development resources.

Bloomberg also offers internships to provide an unparalleled combination of learning, networking, and project responsibilities. The internship programme aims to provide first-hand exposure to its business and unique culture, and is filled with training, seminars, senior leader speaker series, philanthropic events, and much more.

Candidates apply online on Bloomberg's career website. The interview process will depend on the business area they have applied to, but typically involves a video and/or telephone interview followed by assessment days and in-person interviews. Bloomberg hire on a rolling basis, so early application is advised.

GRADUATE VACANCIES IN 2025

ENGINEERING
FINANCE
SALES
TECHNOLOGY

NUMBER OF VACANCIES

350 graduate jobs

LOCATIONS OF VACANCIES

STARTING SALARY FOR 2025

£Competitive

Plus competitive bonuses.

WORK EXPERIENCE

INSIGHT COURSES | DEGREE PLACEMENTS | SUMMER INTERNSHIPS

UNIVERSITY PROMOTIONS DURING 2024-2025

ASTON, BATH, BIRMINGHAM, BRISTOL, CITY UNIVERSITY LONDON, DURHAM, EDINBURGH, EXETER, IMPERIAL COLLEGE LONDON, KING'S COLLEGE LONDON, LANCASTER, LONDON SCHOOL OF ECONOMICS, MANCHESTER, NOTTINGHAM, QUEEN MARY LONDON, SCHOOL OF AFRICAN STUDIES, SOUTHAMPTON, ST ANDREWS, UNIVERSITY COLLEGE LONDON, WARWICK

Please check with your university careers service for full details of Bloomberg's local promotions and events.

APPLICATION DEADLINE

Year-round recruitment

FURTHER INFORMATION

www.Top100GraduateEmployers.com

*Register now for the latest news, local promotions, work experience and graduate vacancies at **Bloomberg**.*

AIRWAYS

emerging.talent@ba.com

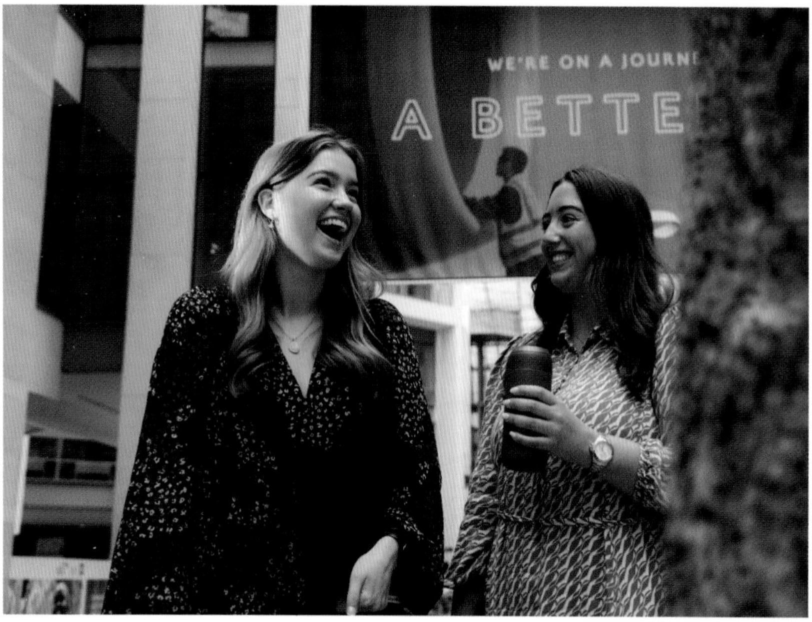

British Airways launched the world's first international scheduled air service between London and Paris in 1919 and today are a leading global airline, flying to over 200 destinations across more than 80 countries. BA lead the industry with their environmental commitment to become carbon net zero by 2050.

The UK flag carrier offers a variety of graduate schemes across data science, finance, commercial, management and engineering. These programmes offer graduates the opportunity to complete rotational placements with genuine decision-making responsibility, working on projects that sit at the very heart of the business. The schemes offer an excellent opportunity to explore a career in a wide variety of sectors within aviation with hands-on practical and strategic experience. Being a part of the graduate community gives the opportunity to engage with graduates from all schemes in the business and learn from former graduates who are now in senior management positions.

British Airways graduates can get involved with the sustainability vision and support with community investment programmes, taking part in fundraising challenges for partnership charities which are close to the company's heart. And not to mention access to heavily discounted flights to go globe-trotting around the world.

British Airways also offer 10-week summer internships and 11-month placements for undergraduate students who want to build a lasting relationship with the brand. These are fantastic development opportunities for young people, with the chance to stay on as a campus ambassador on their return to university. Taking the first step into working can be daunting, but with British Airways young people are able to develop and experience exciting new horizons in an environment that nurtures every possibility.

GRADUATE VACANCIES IN 2025

- ENGINEERING
- FINANCE
- GENERAL MANAGEMENT
- LOGISTICS
- TECHNOLOGY

NUMBER OF VACANCIES

100 graduate jobs

LOCATIONS OF VACANCIES

STARTING SALARY FOR 2025

£33,000-£35,200

WORK EXPERIENCE

- INSIGHT COURSES
- DEGREE PLACEMENTS
- SUMMER INTERNSHIPS

UNIVERSITY PROMOTIONS DURING 2024-2025

ASTON, BATH, BIRMINGHAM, BRISTOL, BRUNEL, CARDIFF, CITY, COVENTRY, EDINBURGH, EXETER, GLASGOW, HERTFORDSHIRE, IMPERIAL COLLEGE LONDON, KENT, KING'S COLLEGE LONDON, KINGSTON, LANCASTER, LIVERPOOL, LIVERPOOL JOHN MOORES, LONDON, LOUGHBOROUGH, LSE, MANCHESTER, NOTTINGHAM, QUEEN MARY LONDON, ROYAL HOLLOWAY LONDON, SHEFFIELD HALLAM, SOUTHAMPTON, STRATHCLYDE, SURREY, UNIVERSITY COLLEGE LONDON, UNIVERSITY OF WEST LONDON, WARWICK

MINIMUM ENTRY REQUIREMENTS

2.2 Degree

Relevant degree required for some roles.

APPLICATION DEADLINE

November 2024

FURTHER INFORMATION

www.Top100GraduateEmployers.com

*Register now for the latest news, local promotions, work experience and graduate vacancies at **British Airways**.*

capgemini.com/gb-en/careers/career-paths

CapgeminiUK | graduate.careers.uk@capgemini.com
@CapgeminiUK | linkedin.com/company/capgemini
@Capgemini_UK | youtube.com/@CapgeminiGlobal

Capgemini

Capgemini is a diverse organisation of 340,000 team members in more than 50 countries. With its strong 55-year heritage and deep industry expertise, Capgemini is trusted by its clients to provide strategy and design to operations, fuelled by cloud, data, AI, connectivity, software, digital engineering and platforms.

Capgemini offers graduate opportunities across consulting, technology, and engineering. There are roles in business and data analysis, software development, cyber security, creative & design, project management and more, spanning a broad range of industries including public sector, manufacturing, and retail. The two-year Empower Programme is a structured development programme offering professional skill building, clear communication, robust support, mentoring and role specific training. Graduates work with clients on innovative projects, collaborating with cross-functional teams to provide solutions to complex challenges and drive digital transformation. They welcome applications from all degrees, although some roles have specific requirements.

The Accelerate Programme is designed for talented graduates who are looking for a role where they can combine technology, data science and creative design to help clients solve complex business and technology challenges. Joining as an associate consultant, graduates are exposed to a range of sectors, after which they will specialise in one of the Capabilities and sectors within Capgemini Invent.

All graduates can access over 250,000 learning resources, technical training, and industry certifications. This is driven by Capgemini's digital learning platform 'Next' and their 'learning for all' mindset. Capgemini supports and encourages graduates to take ownership of their careers and have role autonomy. Both programmes give graduates the opportunity to network and build their personal brand, helping early talent to thrive in their careers.

GRADUATE VACANCIES IN 2025
- CONSULTING
- ENGINEERING
- FINANCE
- SALES
- TECHNOLOGY

NUMBER OF VACANCIES
300+ graduate jobs

LOCATIONS OF VACANCIES

STARTING SALARY FOR 2025
£30,000+

WORK EXPERIENCE
DEGREE PLACEMENTS | SUMMER INTERNSHIPS

UNIVERSITY PROMOTIONS DURING 2024-2025
ASTON, BATH, BIRMINGHAM, BRIGHTON, BRISTOL, BRUNEL, COVENTRY, DURHAM, EDINBURGH, EXETER, GLASGOW, GLASGOW CALEDONIAN, IMPERIAL COLLEGE LONDON, KEELE, KING'S COLLEGE LONDON, LEEDS, LEICESTER, LIVERPOOL, LOUGHBOROUGH, LSE, MANCHESTER, NOTTINGHAM, NOTTINGHAM TRENT, QUEEN MARY LONDON, SHEFFIELD, SHEFFIELD HALLAM, ST ANDREWS, SUSSEX, SWANSEA, UNIVERSITY COLLEGE LONDON, WARWICK

MINIMUM ENTRY REQUIREMENTS
Relevant degree required for some roles.

APPLICATION DEADLINE
Year-round recruitment

FURTHER INFORMATION
www.Top100GraduateEmployers.com
Register now for the latest news, local promotions, work experience and graduate vacancies at ***Capgemini.***

CROWNE PLAZA

Civil Service
Fast Stream

faststream.gov.uk

@FastStreamUK FastStream
linkedin.com/company/civil-service-fast-stream
@CivilServiceFastStream youtube.com/theFastStreamUK

The Civil Service supports the government to implement its policies on behalf of every community across the UK. The award-winning Fast Stream is the leadership and management programme that equips talented graduates with the knowledge, skills and networks to operate effectively across the Civil Service.

The Fast Stream is a unique career development path. Launching two new schemes this year – cyber security and risk management – it offers proactive and ambitious graduates a choice of 17 different schemes. All of which are designed to help accelerate progression to senior roles in the Civil Service. With opportunities nationwide, each scheme offers high-quality training and on-the-job learning, enabling Fast Streamers to build practical skills. Fast Streamers gain a breadth and depth of experience, putting their knowledge into practice across a range of government department postings. They are encouraged to take ownership of their development, pursuing a career path within a government profession.

While the Fast Stream continues to offer opportunities for graduates across all degree subjects and backgrounds, the Civil Service is keen to attract more people with STEM degrees. STEM graduates have a crucial part to play in realising the vision of building a skilled, innovative and ambitious Civil Service equipped for the future.

Fast Streamers are valued members of the wider Civil Service community, where people of all ages, cultures and backgrounds are empowered to develop their skills, knowledge and experience. They make an impact every day, helping to deliver vital public services and government operations by shaping decisions that affect everyone's lives. A range of Fast Stream networks offer a vibrant social life around work as well as enabling graduates to make lasting, professional connections.

GRADUATE VACANCIES IN 2025
- ACCOUNTANCY
- ENGINEERING
- FINANCE
- HUMAN RESOURCES
- PROPERTY
- PURCHASING
- RESEARCH & DEVELOPMENT
- TECHNOLOGY

NUMBER OF VACANCIES
1,000 graduate jobs

LOCATIONS OF VACANCIES

STARTING SALARY FOR 2025
£31,186
2025 salary will be confirmed on the Fast Stream website.

WORK EXPERIENCE
SUMMER INTERNSHIPS

UNIVERSITY PROMOTIONS DURING 2024-2025
Please check with your university careers service for full details of the Civil Service's local promotions and events.

MINIMUM ENTRY REQUIREMENTS
2.2 Degree

APPLICATION DEADLINE
7th November 2024

FURTHER INFORMATION
www.Top100GraduateEmployers.com
*Register now for the latest news, local promotions, work experience and graduate vacancies at the **Civil Service**.*

Civil Service
Fast Stream
Grow like nowhere else
BOOST
YOUR
KNOWLEDGE
SHAPE NATIONWIDE CHANGE
Graduate Leadership and Management
Development Programme
Nationwide Opportunities
Go further, sooner. Own your development on this career-accelerating programme. Gaining real-world skills and experience through high-quality training and postings across government, you'll put what you learn into practice, on work that impacts our nation. We're here to grow tomorrow's leaders and managers, building a brilliant and modern Civil Service for a fast-changing world. And you could help tackle some of our biggest challenges.
Get future-ready at faststream.gov.uk

CLYDE&CO

careers.clydeco.com/en/early-careers

earlycareers@clydeco.com

@clydecoearlycareers

linkedin.com/company/clydeco

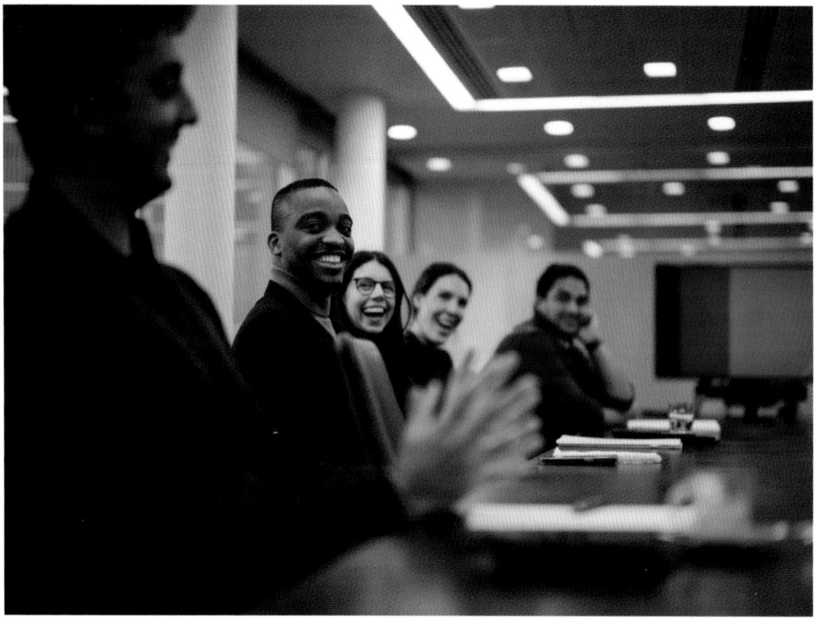

Clyde & Co is a global law firm providing a complete service to clients in core sectors of insurance, transport, energy, infrastructure and trade & commodities. With over 5,000 people operating from over 60 offices, across six continents, Clyde & Co is committed to creating successful outcomes for their clients.

Most of Clyde & Co's trainees are individuals who have impressed the firm through their vacation schemes or through internal recruitment from their paralegal population. Trainees will work with household-name clients, spend time in overseas offices, and take up secondments in areas of specific interest. Clyde & Co seek out early talent with ambition, independent thinking, curiosity and commitment, and will help trainees harness their skills to create a career without boundaries.

Whether fresh out of university or switching careers to follow a long-held dream, the paralegal academy is a way into a legal career for everyone. Trainees join the most extensive casualty practice in the UK, working with some of the best casualty experts in the industry to provide service-based quality while utilising futuristic technologies. Future trainees at Clyde & Co will complete sponsored study as well as receiving a maintenance grant.

In addition, Clyde & Co's vacation schemes are the perfect opportunity for those wanting to experience life with the firm. Participants spend two weeks getting to know trainees, associates and partners. The firm also offer two virtual work experience programmes, recognising the challenges that students face when trying to access a legal career. The early careers programmes are open in 16 countries. With a truly worldwide presence in sectors critical to global infrastructure, Clyde & Co has a network of professionals that will help students and graduates interested in law to achieve their ambition.

GRADUATE VACANCIES IN 2025

LAW

NUMBER OF VACANCIES

50 graduate jobs

For training contracts starting in 2027.

LOCATIONS OF VACANCIES

Vacancies also available in Europe, the USA, Asia and elsewhere in the world.

STARTING SALARY FOR 2025

£24,000-£47,000

WORK EXPERIENCE

INSIGHT COURSES | DEGREE PLACEMENTS | SUMMER INTERNSHIPS

UNIVERSITY PROMOTIONS DURING 2024-2025

ABERDEEN, ASTON, BELFAST, BIRMINGHAM, BRISTOL, CARDIFF, CITY, DUNDEE, DURHAM, EDINBURGH, ESSEX, EXETER, GLASGOW, GLASGOW CALEDONIAN, KENT, KING'S COLLEGE LONDON, LANCASTER, LEEDS, LEICESTER, LIVERPOOL, LIVERPOOL JOHN MOORES, LSE, MANCHESTER, MIDDLESEX, NEWCASTLE, NOTTINGHAM, NOTTINGHAM TRENT, OXFORD, QUEEN MARY LONDON, QUEEN'S UNIVERSITY, SHEFFIELD, SOAS LONDON, SOUTHAMPTON, ST ANDREWS, STRATHCLYDE, UEA, UNIVERSITY COLLEGE LONDON, WARWICK, WESTMINSTER, YORK

MINIMUM ENTRY REQUIREMENTS

2.1 Degree

APPLICATION DEADLINE

6th January 2025

FURTHER INFORMATION

www.Top100GraduateEmployers.com

Register now for the latest news, local promotions, work experience and graduate vacancies at Clyde & Co.

CLYDE&CO
Reshape your future with us.
We offer brilliant opportunities to develop your skills and experience, working on exciting cases alongside some of the most respected and talented lawyers in their field.
You'll be encouraged and supported to realise your full potential, actively participating and collaborating with senior fee earners and partners, with exposure to clients as much as possible.
If you're looking to develop your career and are committed to delivering exceptional outcomes, explore our opportunities today.
Go further. Search Early Careers at Clyde & Co.
careers.clydeco.com
clydecoearlycareers
Success & Beyond

Deloitte.

deloitte.co.uk/careers

DeloitteUK
@DeloitteCareers
linkedin.com/company/deloitte
@Deloitte_UK
youtube.com/DeloitteCareersUK

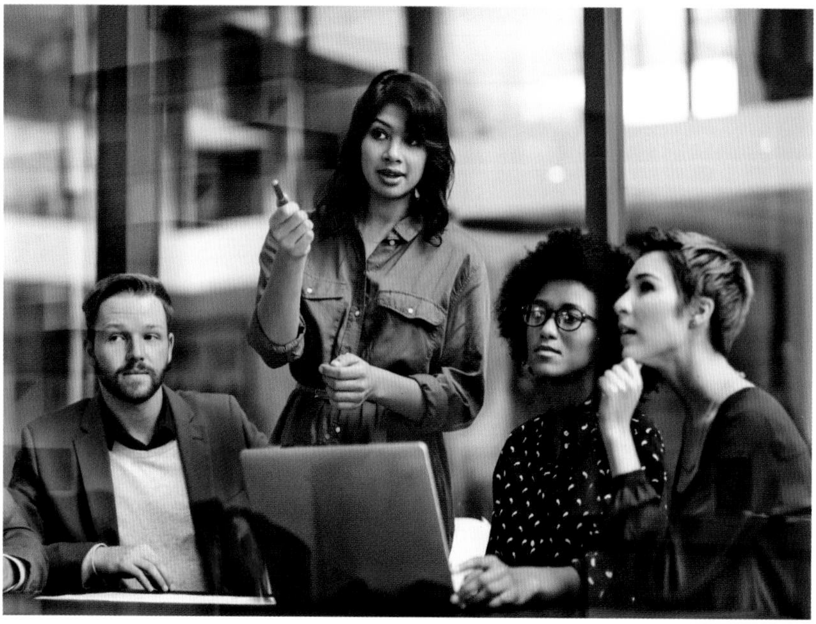

For more than 175 years, Deloitte has offered professional services to organisations – from the Global 500 to private businesses – to build better futures. Deloitte makes its impact through collaboration. All around the world, their colleagues spark positive progress for their clients, people and society.

By joining Deloitte, graduates will be connected to inspiring colleagues across the globe. They offer a huge range of early career opportunities, where graduates can choose their own impact and build a future that suits them. From audit and assurance, tax consulting and legal to technology and consulting, Deloitte are delivering end-to-end programmes, turning complex challenges into opportunity and redesigning a more connected future.

Deloitte's graduate programmes offer more than a training scheme. With a permanent position, market-leading salary and tailored benefits, there are endless opportunities for growth and development. Participants will study towards recognised professional qualifications, have an unrivalled client list and fast progression on a structured career path. In every one of their twenty-two offices across the UK and offshore, graduates will find opportunities to work with local and global businesses, connect with teams across the world and develop both their technical and personal skills.

Deloitte offer a range of apprenticeship and placement schemes across their key business areas. Their Spring Into Deloitte work experience, Summer Vacation Scheme and Industrial Placement programmes are designed to help participants explore potential career options and gain hands-on experience.

From day one, graduates will be supported to make serious contributions to projects and the business. They will connect with colleagues who share a common purpose to tackle businesses' biggest challenges.

GRADUATE VACANCIES IN 2025

- ACCOUNTANCY
- CONSULTING
- FINANCE
- HUMAN RESOURCES
- LAW
- PROPERTY
- TECHNOLOGY

NUMBER OF VACANCIES
1,500+ graduate jobs

LOCATIONS OF VACANCIES

STARTING SALARY FOR 2025
£Competitive

WORK EXPERIENCE
INSIGHT COURSES | DEGREE PLACEMENTS | SUMMER INTERNSHIPS

UNIVERSITY PROMOTIONS DURING 2024-2025
Please check with your university careers service for full details of Deloitte's local promotions and events.

MINIMUM ENTRY REQUIREMENTS
2.1 Degree,
104 UCAS points

APPLICATION DEADLINE
Please see website for full details. Deloitte recruits on a rolling basis.

FURTHER INFORMATION
www.Top100GraduateEmployers.com
Register now for the latest news, local promotions, work experience and graduate vacancies at ***Deloitte.***

careers.db.com/students-graduates

DeutscheBankCareers | uk.graduatequeries@db.com
@DeutscheBank | linkedin.com/company/deutsche-bank
@DeutscheBank | youtube.com/DeutscheBank

For over 150 years, Deutsche Bank has been dedicated to their client's lasting success at home and abroad. As the Global Hausbank, Deutsche Bank provides financial services to companies, governments, institutional investors, small and medium-sized businesses, and private individuals.

The bank has four core businesses: the Corporate Bank, the Investment Bank, the Private Bank and the Asset Management business (DWS). All of which are well positioned to respond to trends that will shape the economy, and to deliver their combined expertise to clients. Deutsche Bank's Graduate Programme is a year-long comprehensive programme that provides graduates with ongoing professional and technical training, and a network of support to help them develop the skills they need to take initiative and pioneer real solutions. Whether embarking on a Graduate Programme in one of the business divisions, or in an infrastructure team like Technology, Data & Innovation, Chief Risk Office or Human Resources, graduates benefit from Deutsche Bank's collaborative culture.

Deutsche Bank's nine-week Summer Internship Programme and 3-6 month Seasonal Internship Programme is designed to enable early talent to develop skills that will help them succeed, through formal training and continuous support. These interns will learn first-hand how and what the bank deliver for clients worldwide and quickly gain the confidence it takes to impact real projects.

Deutsche Bank's Early Careers programmes are designed to support students and graduates develop the skills and knowledge they need to take charge of their career. Supported by a global network of talented colleagues, graduates are encouraged to work together while being given the autonomy to achieve their goals. As graduates grow, they will continue to benefit from a variety of in-person and on-demand training in an environment which encourages diverse careers.

GRADUATE VACANCIES IN 2025

HUMAN RESOURCES
INVESTMENT BANKING
TECHNOLOGY

NUMBER OF VACANCIES

100+ graduate jobs

LOCATIONS OF VACANCIES

STARTING SALARY FOR 2025

£Competitive

Plus a sign-on bonus.

WORK EXPERIENCE

INSIGHT COURSES | DEGREE PLACEMENTS | SUMMER INTERNSHIPS

UNIVERSITY PROMOTIONS DURING 2024-2025

BIRMINGHAM, BRISTOL, CAMBRIDGE, DURHAM, EDINBURGH, IMPERIAL COLLEGE LONDON, KING'S COLLEGE LONDON, LEEDS, LONDON BUSINESS SCHOOL, LOUGHBOROUGH, LSE, MANCHESTER, NOTTINGHAM, OXFORD, QUEEN MARY LONDON, SHEFFIELD, ST ANDREWS, UNIVERSITY COLLEGE LONDON, WARWICK

Please check with your university careers service for full details of Deutsche Bank's local promotions and events.

MINIMUM ENTRY REQUIREMENTS

2.1 Degree

APPLICATION DEADLINE

September 2024 - February 2025

FURTHER INFORMATION

www.Top100GraduateEmployers.com

Register now for the latest news, local promotions, work experience and graduate vacancies at ***Deutsche Bank.***

Think bigger.
Think bolder.
Think Deutsche Bank.
careers.db.com
Thinking about your next steps? Our Insight, Internship and Graduate Programmes offer an incredible platform for a career in finance. Designed to support your development, they'll give you the skills you'll need for a successful future.
Discover our Early Careers opportunities.
Scan our QR code to learn more.

DIAGEO

diageo.com/en/careers/early-careers

linkedin.com/company/diageo

@diageo youtube.com/diageo

With over 200 brands sold in nearly 180 countries, Diageo are the world's leading premium drinks company. Every day, over 30,000 people come together to create the magic behind their much loved brands. From iconic names to innovative newcomers – the brands Diageo is building are rooted in culture and local communities.

Diageo's founders, such as Arthur Guinness, John Walker and Elizabeth Cumming, were visionary entrepreneurs whose brilliant minds helped shape the alcohol industry. Through Diageo's people, their legacy lives on. By joining Diageo, individuals will collaborate, explore, and innovate, challenging and being challenged. Together with passionate people from across the world, they will build brands consumers love.

Diageo's graduate programmes challenge, inspire, and provide the support needed to kick-start a rewarding career. As a graduate at Diageo, individuals will help build iconic brands consumers love, such as Guinness, Baileys, and Johnnie Walker. By aiming high, graduates will be supported to explore, learn, and grow while collaborating with passionate people from all corners of the world.

Diageo's graduate schemes last for 1-3 years and are available across its regions: Great Britain, Ireland, Southern Europe, and Turkey.

Diageo encourages graduates to come as they are, share their ideas, and learn from others. By bringing passion, curiosity, and a desire to learn and grow relentlessly, graduates will be celebrated for their contributions to progress and will enjoy an attractive benefits and rewards package.

Supported by a buddy, they will learn from experienced and knowledgeable colleagues. Graduates will develop leadership skills and knowledge through formal and informal training. From day one, graduates will make a real contribution to the business and industry.

GRADUATE VACANCIES IN 2025

- ENGINEERING
- FINANCE
- HUMAN RESOURCES
- MARKETING
- SALES
- TECHNOLOGY

NUMBER OF VACANCIES
25 graduate jobs

LOCATIONS OF VACANCIES

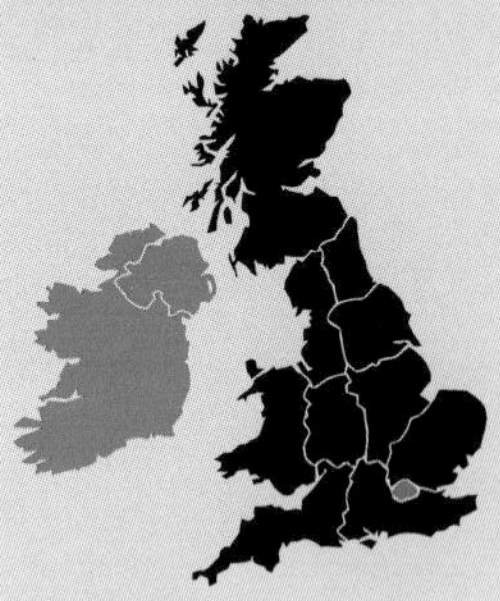

Vacancies also available in Europe.

STARTING SALARY FOR 2025
£37,780
Plus an annual bonus incentive plan.

UNIVERSITY PROMOTIONS DURING 2024-2025
ASTON, BIRMINGHAM, CITY, HERIOT-WATT, IMPERIAL COLLEGE LONDON, KING'S COLLEGE LONDON, NOTTINGHAM, NOTTINGHAM TRENT, QUEEN MARY LONDON, QUEEN'S UNIVERSITY BELFAST, STRATHCLYDE
Please check with your university careers service for full details of Diageo's local promotions and events.

MINIMUM ENTRY REQUIREMENTS
Relevant degree required for some roles.

APPLICATION DEADLINE
Mid-November

FURTHER INFORMATION
www.Top100GraduateEmployers.com
*Register now for the latest news, local promotions, work experience and graduate vacancies at **Diageo**.*

DLA PIPER

earlycareers.dlapiper.com/uk

earlycareers@dlapiper.com

linkedin.com/company/dla-piper

@DLAPiperCareers youtube.com/dlapiper

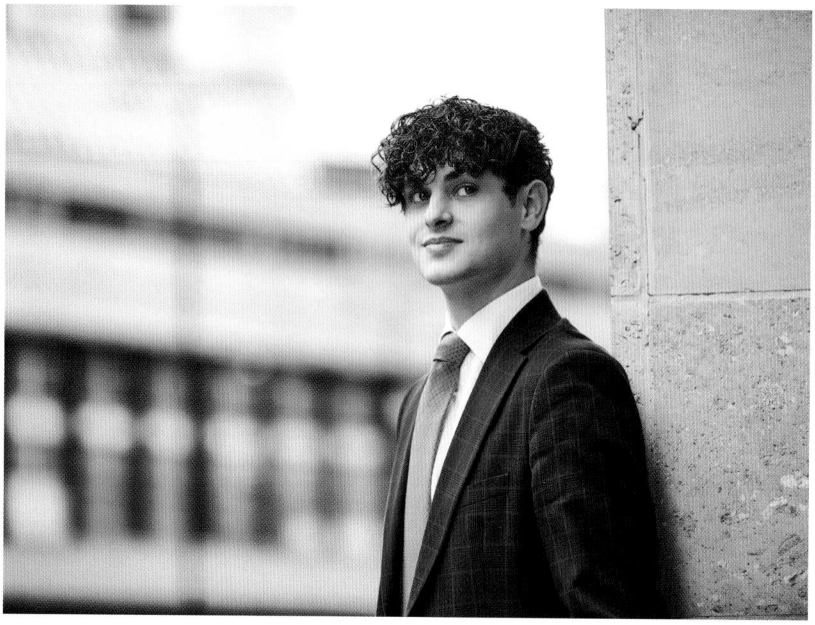

DLA Piper are redefining what an international law firm can be. With over 90 offices in more than 40 countries, they offer global careers without limits. At DLA Piper, trainees find the most interesting work, experience the riches of other cultures, and enjoy the complexity of an interconnected world.

At DLA Piper, trainees define the impact they make, and the firm invites them to help shape the future of law. They offer a three-and-a-half-week summer internship programme, which begins with a three-day induction event held in the DLA Piper London office, followed by three-weeks of working in two practice groups at a chosen office location. The firm recruits interns into the following UK offices: Birmingham, Edinburgh, Leeds, London, and Manchester. Applicants can apply for the programme regardless of degree background. Law students must be a second-year student on a three-year course, or a third-year student on a four-year course; non-law applicants must be in their final year of study or already graduated.

Successful completion of the summer internship will result in a place on DLA Piper's international training programme, where trainees are sponsored to attend a Masters level preparatory course which includes the SQE1 and SQE2 examinations – which are required to qualify as a solicitor. For non-law degree joiners a law conversion course will be sponsored before the SQE preparatory course. Trainees will start a two-year programme by participating in the international training programme induction week held in London.

Across the two-year programme, trainees undertake four, six-month rotations within DLA Piper's practice groups. There are plenty of opportunities for client and international secondments, as well as continual learning and development with training sessions and a strong support network of supervisors and buddies.

GRADUATE VACANCIES IN 2025

LAW

NUMBER OF VACANCIES

50+ graduate jobs

For training contracts starting in 2027.

LOCATIONS OF VACANCIES

Vacancies also available elsewhere in the world.

STARTING SALARY FOR 2025

£34,000-£50,000

Paid SQE fees and course fees for law conversion and Masters courses. Paid visa costs where required. Plus, maintenance grants ranging from £10,000-£17,000 to support graduate and master studies.

WORK EXPERIENCE

INSIGHT COURSES | SUMMER INTERNSHIPS

UNIVERSITY PROMOTIONS DURING 2024-2025

ABERDEEN, ASTON, BIRMINGHAM, BRISTOL, CAMBRIDGE, COVENTRY, DURHAM, EDINBURGH, GLASGOW, GLASGOW CALEDONIAN, IMPERIAL COLLEGE LONDON, KING'S COLLEGE LONDON, LEEDS, LIVERPOOL, LSE, MANCHESTER, NOTTINGHAM, OXFORD, QUEEN MARY LONDON, SHEFFIELD, STRATHCLYDE, UNIVERSITY COLLEGE LONDON, WARWICK, YORK

Please check with your university careers service for full details of DLA Piper's local promotions and events.

APPLICATION DEADLINE

Please see website for full details. Recruitment is on a rolling basis.

FURTHER INFORMATION

www.Top100GraduateEmployers.com

*Register now for the latest news, local promotions, work experience and graduate vacancies at **DLA Piper**.*

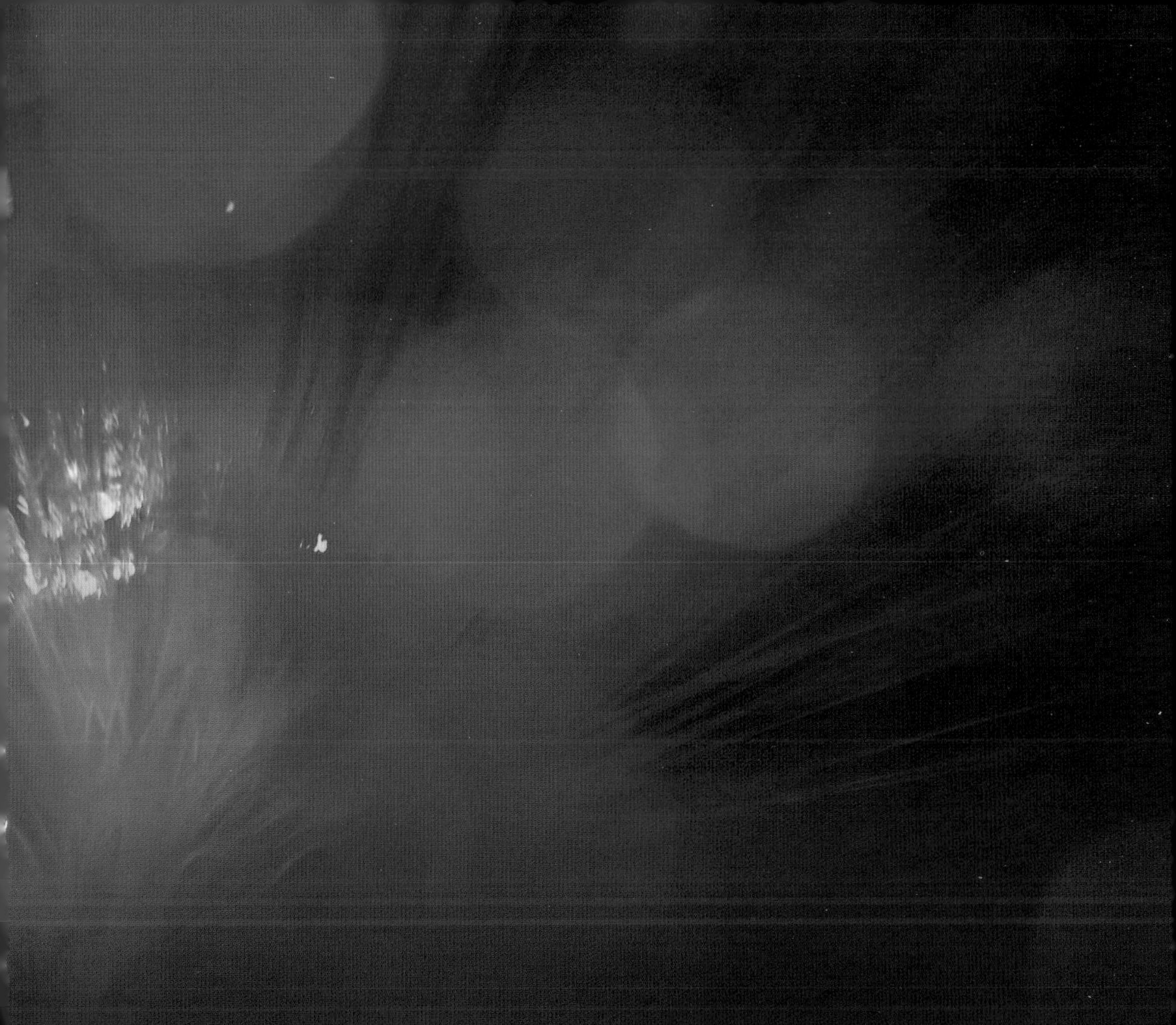

dyson

careers.dyson.com/early-careers

graduates@dyson.com
linkedin.com/company/dyson
@dyson youtube.com/@dyson

Dyson is a global technology enterprise. They solve the problems others choose to ignore, with surprising new inventions that defy convention and work better. Dyson is driven by progress and thrives on the challenge of improvement.

Since inventing the first cyclonic bagless vacuum cleaner – DC01 – in 1993, Dyson has created problem solving technologies in floor care, air purification, hair care, lighting, hand drying, and now audio.

Dyson offer graduate roles in a variety of locations. They believe in maximising potential through real-life experiences and graduates are trusted with real work and responsibility from the outset, working on high-profile live projects across the business. They have the opportunity to make a difference to Dyson's future, working directly with senior leaders – many of whom joined Dyson as graduates themselves – and specialist teams across the globe.

Dyson places great importance on nurturing new talent through their early careers programmes. The two-year graduate programme offers opportunities to develop both technical and soft skills. Through structured rotations, graduates gain key skills and a comprehensive understanding of the business. A series of development sessions cover a broad range of topics, with the goal of preparing graduates for future success at Dyson. Dyson offers both summer and year-long placements for students in their engineering and group functions.

The internship programme connects academic theory with practical experience, and students gain valuable insights into professional applications through mentorships and exposure to cutting-edge practices. Regardless of which early careers programme, graduates and students will network with senior leaders and continue into the Dyson talent pipeline following completion of their programme.

GRADUATE VACANCIES IN 2025
ENGINEERING
MARKETING
RESEARCH & DEVELOPMENT
TECHNOLOGY

NUMBER OF VACANCIES
No fixed quota

LOCATIONS OF VACANCIES

STARTING SALARY FOR 2025
£32,000

WORK EXPERIENCE
DEGREE PLACEMENTS | SUMMER INTERNSHIPS

UNIVERSITY PROMOTIONS DURING 2024-2025
BATH, GLASGOW, IMPERIAL COLLEGE LONDON, LOUGHBOROUGH, LSE, NOTTINGHAM, SHEFFIELD, SOUTHAMPTON, UNIVERSITY COLLEGE LONDON, WARWICK
Please check with your university careers service for full details of Dyson's local promotions and events.

MINIMUM ENTRY REQUIREMENTS
Relevant degree required for some roles.

APPLICATION DEADLINE
Early 2025

FURTHER INFORMATION
www.Top100GraduateEmployers.com
Register now for the latest news, local promotions, work experience and graduate vacancies at ***Dyson.***

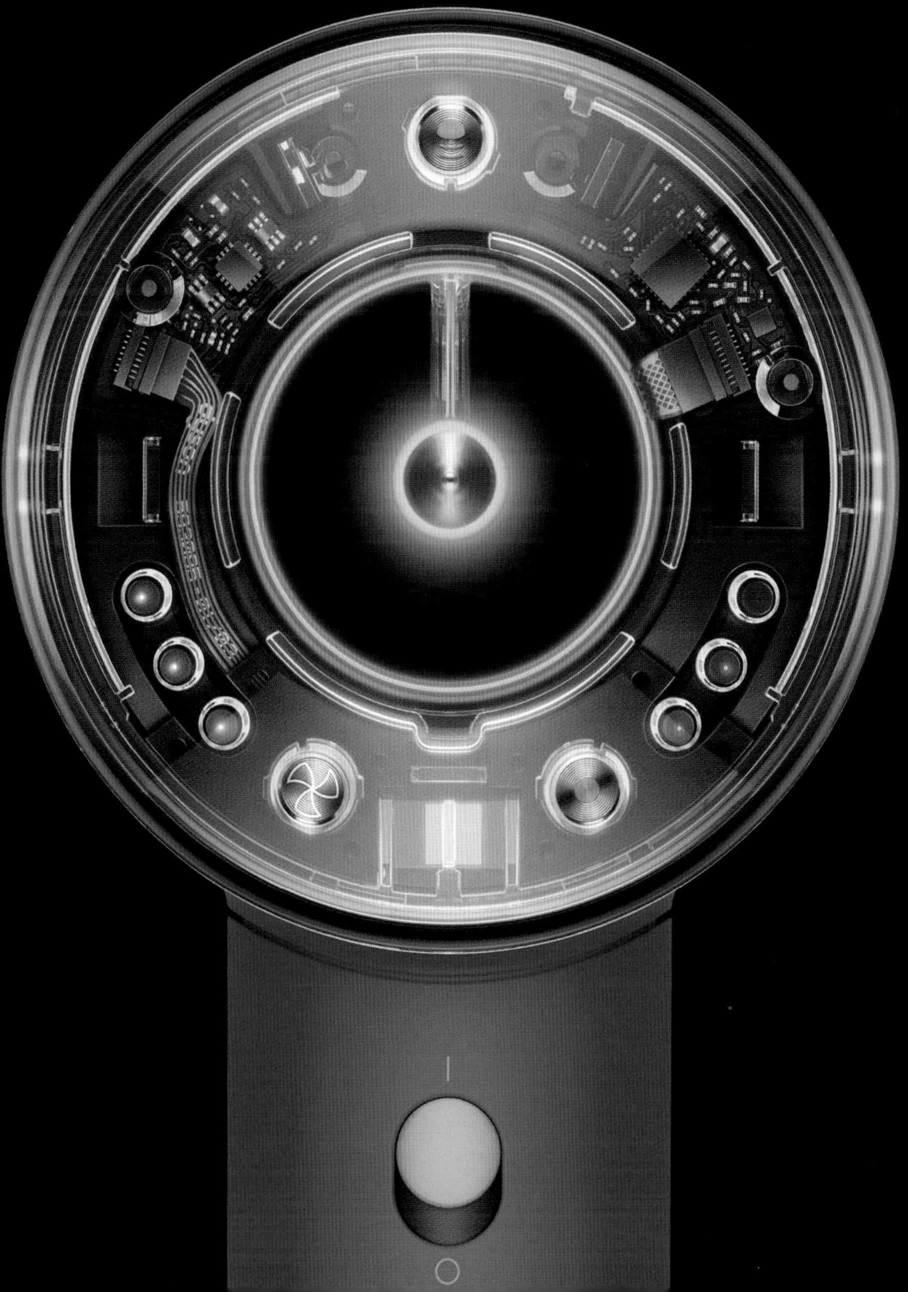

Enterprise Mobility™

careers.enterprise.co.uk

sayhello@em.com

enterprisemobilitycareerseurope · linkedin.com/company/enterprise-mobility-

@enterprisemobility.careers.uk · youtube.com/@enterprisemobilitycareersemea

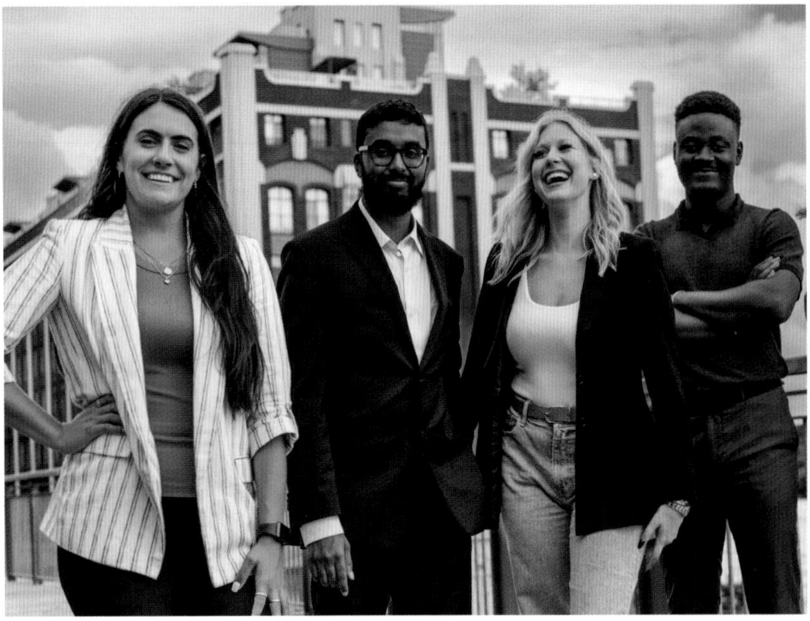

Enterprise Mobility™ is an organisation that's grown from a pioneering idea and seven cars to a global mobility leader. Staying true to the people-first philosophy that's guided them from day one, their 90,000+ team members are now focused on shaping the mobility experiences of the future.

Enterprise Mobility believes great leaders are made, and as a Graduate Management Trainee, individuals will have the freedom to explore their potential. From their first day, the organisation invests in them within a supportive environment where they will take on real responsibilities, gaining invaluable hands-on experience across all facets of the organisation, including sales, marketing, customer service, finance and operations.

Offering 12-month placements and summer internships, Enterprise Mobility believes that tomorrow's leaders learn by doing. From day one, participants join an environment where they can thrive, gain new experiences, and develop leadership skills to map out their future. While they are busy learning, Enterprise Mobility ensures their efforts are recognised and rewarded.

Whether helping build on existing skills or learning new ones, career development is a top priority for Enterprise Mobility. From classroom settings to on-the-job training and mentorship, there are plenty of opportunities for graduates to refine their skills and prepare for the next step in their career.

Team members and their managers will work closely to create a development plan that matches the specific needs and interests of each trainee. Each day, they will work alongside some of the best in the industry, constantly learning from colleagues who are equally invested in their success. Plus, with their unique promote-from-within culture, graduates will always be making progress in their career – and flourishing in ways never thought possible.

GRADUATE VACANCIES IN 2025

GENERAL MANAGEMENT
RETAIL
SALES

NUMBER OF VACANCIES

1,300 graduate jobs

LOCATIONS OF VACANCIES

STARTING SALARY FOR 2025

£28,000

Plus performance-based bonuses following completion of graduate programme, and relocation allowance if applicable.

WORK EXPERIENCE

INSIGHT COURSES | DEGREE PLACEMENTS | SUMMER INTERNSHIPS

UNIVERSITY PROMOTIONS DURING 2024-2025

ABERDEEN, ABERYSTWYTH, ASTON, BANGOR, BATH, BIRMINGHAM, BOURNEMOUTH, BRADFORD, BRIGHTON, BRISTOL, BRUNEL, CARDIFF, CARDIFF METROPOLITAN, CITY, COVENTRY, DERBY, DUNDEE, DURHAM, EDINBURGH, EDINBURGH NAPIER, ESSEX, EXETER, FALMOUTH, GLASGOW, GLASGOW CALEDONIAN, HERIOT-WATT, HUDDERSFIELD, HULL, KEELE, KENT, LANCASTER, LEEDS, LEICESTER, LINCOLN, LIVERPOOL, LIVERPOOL JOHN MOORES, LOUGHBOROUGH, MANCHESTER, NEWCASTLE, NORTHUMBRIA, NOTTINGHAM, NOTTINGHAM TRENT, OXFORD BROOKES, PLYMOUTH, PORTSMOUTH, QUEEN MARY LONDON, READING, ROBERT GORDON, ROYAL HOLLOWAY LONDON, SALFORD, SHEFFIELD, SHEFFIELD HALLAM, SOUTHAMPTON, ST ANDREWS, STIRLING, STRATHCLYDE, SUNDERLAND, SURREY, SUSSEX, SWANSEA, UEA, ULSTER, WARWICK, WEST OF ENGLAND (UWE), WINCHESTER, YORK

APPLICATION DEADLINE

Year-round recruitment

FURTHER INFORMATION

www.Top100GraduateEmployers.com

Register now for the latest news, local promotions, work experience and graduate vacancies at ***Enterprise Mobility.***

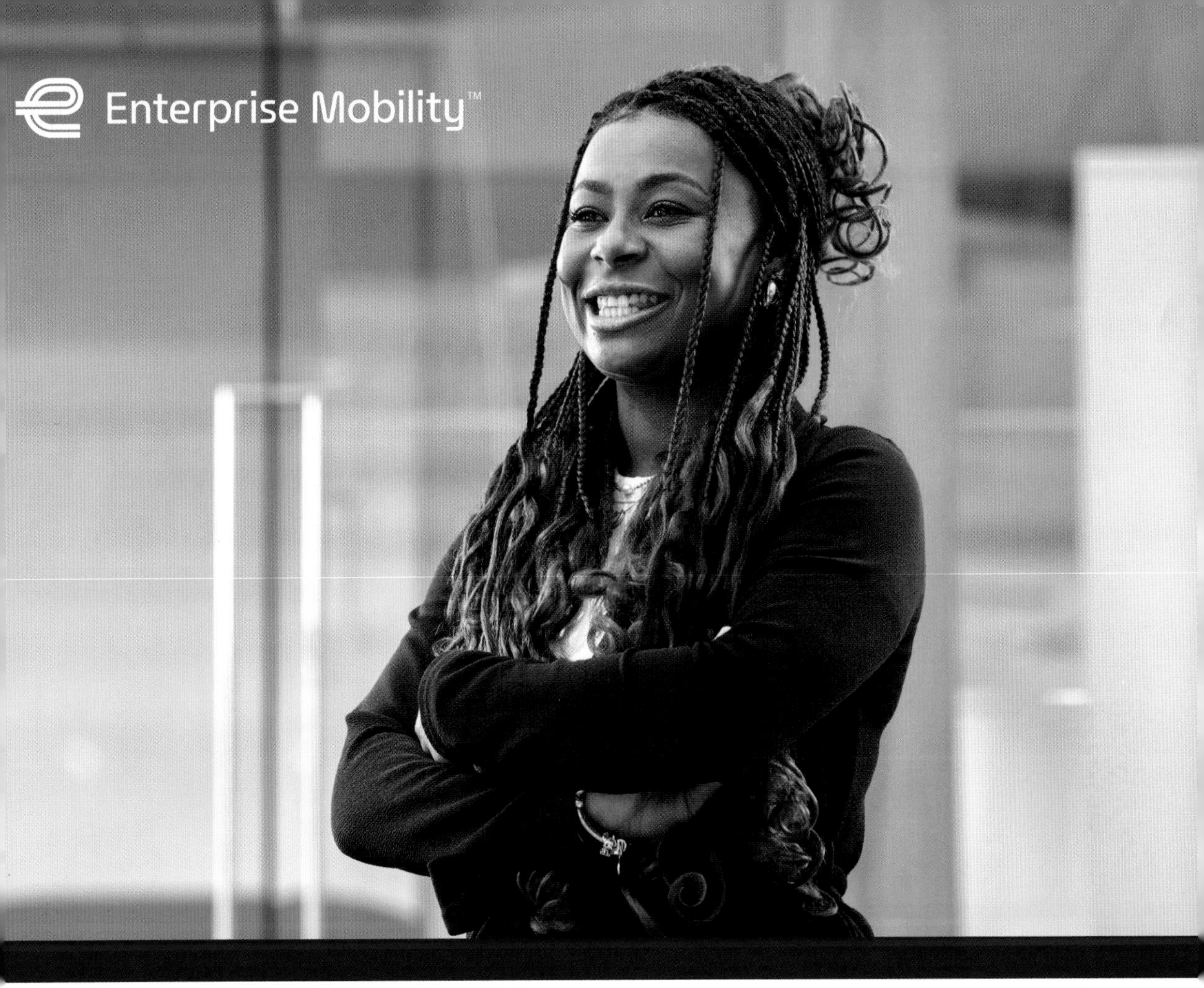
Enterprise Mobility™

EY
Building a better working world

ey.com/uk/students
@EY_CareersUK EYCareersUK
linkedin.com/company/ernstandyoung
@EYUKcareers youtube.com/EYUKCareers

As a professional services organisation, EY help companies make better decisions about business, finance and technology. The organisation has 400,000 people in more than 150 countries, working across four key business areas – Assurance, Consulting, Strategy and Transactions, and Tax.

EY transform how businesses work by using the latest technology across different sectors, helping clients find innovative solutions to their complex problems. Their purpose is building a better working world, with the help of their people. At EY, people are empowered with the right mindsets and skills to navigate what's next, become the transformative leaders the world needs, pursue careers as unique as they are, and build their own exceptional EY experiences.

EY offers graduate programmes within their four key business areas, alongside opportunities for work experience, summer internships, and industrial placements. As motivated and passionate members of the organisation, interns and graduates will have a personal impact – no matter which area they join. EY provides the tools, networks, experiences and opportunities for graduates to learn, lead, innovate and grow. Successful applicants will receive dedicated, structured training, a careers counsellor, a buddy, as well as access to innovative technology.

Whether working from home or the office, EY employees are encouraged to find their own ways to achieve the balance and flexibility they deserve. It's all part of adapting to the future working world. EY believe that the ability to invite, leverage and learn from different perspectives is key to delivering for their clients and build a better world for all. Kick-start a career at EY – whether that's for two days, four weeks or three years – on one of their student programmes. EY will prepare students for the world of work and invest in their future from day one.

GRADUATE VACANCIES IN 2025
ACCOUNTANCY
CONSULTING
FINANCE
LAW
TECHNOLOGY

NUMBER OF VACANCIES
1,000+ graduate jobs

LOCATIONS OF VACANCIES

STARTING SALARY FOR 2025
£Competitive

WORK EXPERIENCE
INSIGHT COURSES | DEGREE PLACEMENTS | SUMMER INTERNSHIPS

UNIVERSITY PROMOTIONS DURING 2024-2025
ABERDEEN, ASTON, BATH, BIRMINGHAM, BRISTOL, CAMBRIDGE, CARDIFF, DURHAM, EDINBURGH, EDINBURGH NAPIER, EXETER, GLASGOW, HERIOT-WATT, IMPERIAL COLLEGE LONDON, KING'S COLLEGE LONDON, LANCASTER, LEEDS, LIVERPOOL, LOUGHBOROUGH, LSE, MANCHESTER, NEWCASTLE, NOTTINGHAM, OXFORD, QUEEN'S UNIVERSITY, BELFAST, READING, ROBERT GORDON, SHEFFIELD, SOUTHAMPTON, ST ANDREWS, STRATHCLYDE, ULSTER, UNIVERSITY COLLEGE LONDON, WARWICK, YORK

MINIMUM ENTRY REQUIREMENTS
Relevant degree required for some roles.

APPLICATION DEADLINE
September 2024 - June 2025

FURTHER INFORMATION
www.Top100GraduateEmployers.com
Register now for the latest news, local promotions, work experience and graduate vacancies at ***EY.***

What future are you building towards?
At EY, we have a range of undergraduate and graduate programmes.
When you join us, you'll make an impact from the get-go. You'll have the opportunity to make your mark on how we do business and help our clients evolve while being supported every step of the way.
We'll equip you with the skills, tools, networks and experiences you'll need to build a career you can truly be proud of.
Discover the possibilities and your own potential at EY.
Start your career adventure at EY.
ey.com/uk/students
The better the question.
The better the answer.
The better the world works.
©2024 Ernst & Young LLP. All rights reserved. ED0525
EY
Building a better working world

forv/s mazars

jobs.mazars.co.uk/jobs/early-careers

ForvisMazarsGroup | mcareers@mazars.co.uk
@ForvisMazarsGrp | linkedin.com/company/forvis-mazars-group
@ForvisMazarsGroup | youtube.com/@ForvisMazarsGroup

Forvis Mazars is a leading global professional services network operating in over 100 countries and territories with over 40,000 professionals and are committed to providing an unmatched client experience across audit & assurance, tax, advisory and consulting services.

Forvis Mazars has graduate opportunities available in audit, tax, and advisory for students and recent graduates. These roles are located nationally across 13 of their UK offices, meaning there is an opportunity to suit every individual career pathway. Forvis Mazars offers undergraduates a 12-month placement, based across the UK. Placement students are given a high level of responsibility, supporting on projects with prestigious clients, whilst also being given the opportunity to start their professional qualifications, with the intention to return to Forvis Mazars on a graduate programme after university.

There are a range of internship opportunities available throughout the summer across various service lines. Interns receive professional skills training as well as working on the Forvis Mazars Challenge, working on real-life innovation or sustainability issues. Interns can also convert their internship to a graduate role. There are further opportunities throughout the year for first year students looking to take part in insight days.

Forvis Mazars offer excellent professional skills development and real responsibility from the start, with exposure to prestigious clients and dynamic projects, across a range of sectors. They provide graduates the opportunity to gain a professional qualification whilst earning a competitive salary and gaining invaluable industry experience. They are known as an engine for rapid and consistent career progression, giving ambitious people the opportunity for early responsibility and exposure to an interesting and rewarding portfolio of work.

GRADUATE VACANCIES IN 2025

ACCOUNTANCY
CONSULTING
FINANCE
TECHNOLOGY

NUMBER OF VACANCIES

400 graduate jobs

LOCATIONS OF VACANCIES

STARTING SALARY FOR 2025

£Competitive

WORK EXPERIENCE

INSIGHT COURSES | DEGREE PLACEMENTS | SUMMER INTERNSHIPS

UNIVERSITY PROMOTIONS DURING 2024-2025

ASTON, BATH, BIRMINGHAM, BOURNEMOUTH, BRISTOL, CAMBRIDGE, CARDIFF, CITY, COVENTRY, DURHAM, EDINBURGH, GLASGOW, LANCASTER, LEEDS, LEICESTER, LOUGHBOROUGH, LSE, MANCHESTER, NEWCASTLE, NOTTINGHAM, NOTTINGHAM TRENT, QUEEN MARY LONDON, READING, SHEFFIELD, STRATHCLYDE, SURREY, UNIVERSITY COLLEGE LONDON, WARWICK, YORK

APPLICATION DEADLINE

Year-round recruitment

FURTHER INFORMATION

www.Top100GraduateEmployers.com

*Register now for the latest news, local promotions, work experience and graduate vacancies at **Forvis Mazars**.*

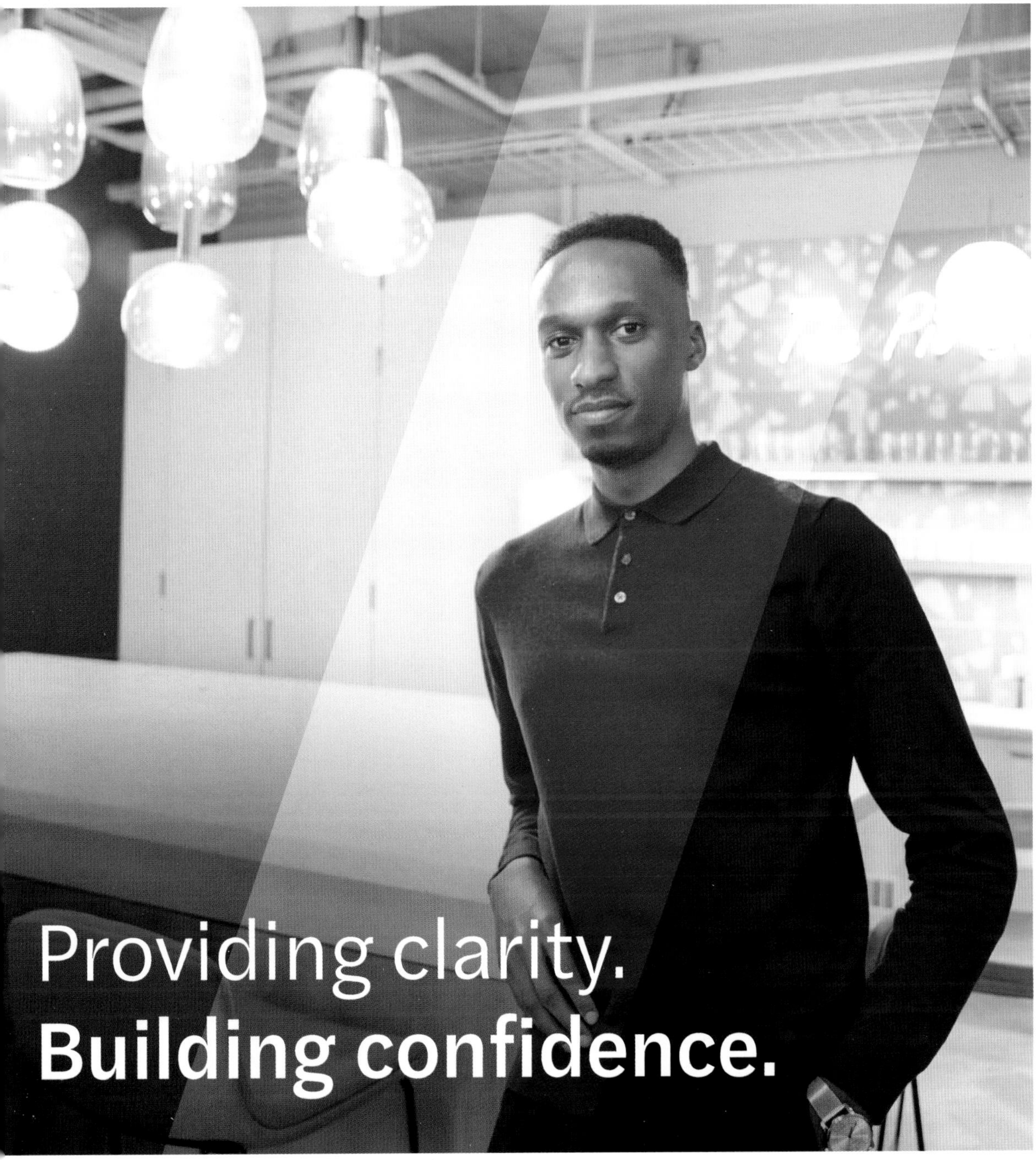
Providing clarity.
Building confidence.

Freshfields

freshfields.com/earlycareers

FreshfieldsGraduates | ukgraduates@freshfields.com

@freshfieldsgrads | linkedin.com/company/freshfields

Freshfields is a leading global law firm with a long-standing track record of supporting the world's largest corporations, financial institutions, and governments in navigating their most complex legal challenges. Shape the future and make a real impact that resonates around the world.

The Freshfields' eight-seat trainee associate programme offers graduates the opportunity to explore diverse areas of commercial law while embarking on a career filled with high-profile and precedent-setting work. Combining on-the-job learning with structured skills development, graduates can expect more collaboration, more opportunity, more variety and more impact. All while building the skills and making the most of the opportunities needed to grow – not just as lawyers, but as people too.

Graduates will rotate teams every three months and be given the opportunity to decide what practice area they would like to experience next. Throughout the programme and beyond, they are empowered to make the most of the opportunities on offer and shape their own journey at the firm. Freshfields' vacation scheme is an exciting way for individuals to gain a practical insight into life at the firm. Interns will join the London office and immerse themselves in the work and culture through engaging with associates and partners, participating in group exercises, and contributing to real projects.

All future trainees at Freshfields will complete the City Consortium Solicitor Training Programme (CCP) with BPP Law School to prepare for the Solicitors Qualifying Examination (SQE). Those who have completed a non-law undergraduate degree must complete the Law Conversion Course (PGDL) before starting the CCP and sitting the SQE exams. The firm sponsors the completion of the CCP and PGDL, as well as providing maintenance grants.

GRADUATE VACANCIES IN 2025

LAW

NUMBER OF VACANCIES

Up to 100 graduate jobs

For training contracts starting in 2027.

LOCATIONS OF VACANCIES

Vacancies also available in Europe, the USA and Asia.

STARTING SALARY FOR 2025

£56,000

Raising to £61,000 in 2nd year of Trainee Associate Programme, and a NQ salary of £150,000.

WORK EXPERIENCE

INSIGHT COURSES | SUMMER INTERNSHIPS

UNIVERSITY PROMOTIONS DURING 2024-2025

Please check with your university careers service for full details of Freshfields' local promotions and events.

MINIMUM ENTRY REQUIREMENTS

2.1 Degree

APPLICATION DEADLINE

14th November 2024 - 13th February 2025

FURTHER INFORMATION

www.Top100GraduateEmployers.com

*Register now for the latest news, local promotions, work experience and graduate vacancies at **Freshfields**.*

google.com/students

Google

GoogleStudents
@GoogleStudents linkedin.com/company/google
@GoogleStudents youtube.com/GoogleStudents

Larry Page and Sergey Brin founded Google in September 1998 with a mission to organise the world's information and make it universally accessible and useful. Since then, Google has grown, and its parent company, Alphabet, has over 182,000 employees worldwide, with a wide range of popular products and platforms.

Google aims to solve problems for everyone, with everyone, and its employees (or "Googlers") build products that help create opportunities for people globally. They bring insight, imagination, and a passion for tackling challenges. It's the people who make Google the unique company it is.

Google hires individuals who are intelligent, driven, and determined, valuing ability over experience. They recruit graduates from diverse disciplines, from humanities and business to engineering and computer science. Ideal candidates demonstrate a passion for the online industry and have actively engaged in their university experience through clubs, societies, or relevant internships. Technical roles within engineering teams may require specific skills. Google recognises that diversity in perspectives, ideas, and cultures leads to the creation of better products and services.

Whether it's providing online marketing consultancy, selling advertising solutions, recruiting new talent, or building products, Google offers full-time roles and internships across various teams, including global customer solutions, sales, people operations, legal, finance, operations, cloud, and engineering. Opportunities include their Associate Product Manager (APM) programme, Associate Product Marketing Manager programme (APMM), the BOLD internship programme, and Spark at Google. With programmes and internships across the globe, there are many opportunities to grow with Google and help create products and services used by billions.

GRADUATE VACANCIES IN 2025
- CONSULTING
- ENGINEERING
- HUMAN RESOURCES
- MARKETING
- SALES
- TECHNOLOGY

NUMBER OF VACANCIES
No fixed quota

LOCATIONS OF VACANCIES

Vacancies also available in Europe.

STARTING SALARY FOR 2025
£Competitive

WORK EXPERIENCE
SUMMER INTERNSHIPS

UNIVERSITY PROMOTIONS DURING 2024-2025
Please check with your university careers service for full details of Google's local promotions and events.

MINIMUM ENTRY REQUIREMENTS
Relevant degree required for some roles.

APPLICATION DEADLINE
Year-round recruitment

FURTHER INFORMATION
www.Top100GraduateEmployers.com
Register now for the latest news, local promotions, work experience and graduate vacancies at ***Google****.*

![Grant Thornton]

trainees.grantthornton.co.uk

@gt_trainees | traineerecruitment@uk.gt.com

linkedin.com/company/grant-thornton-uk-llp

@grantthorntonuk | youtube.com/UKGrantThornton

Grant Thornton UK LLP is part of a global network of independent audit, tax and advisory firms. Their team put quality, inclusion and integrity first and help people in businesses and communities to do what is right and achieve their goals. Personal, proactive, and agile. That's Grant Thornton.

Grant Thornton's three-year graduate programme will take successful applicants from newly graduated to professionally qualified, opening up a world of opportunity. Whether joining in audit, tax or advisory, graduates gain cutting-edge skills and work on a variety of exciting projects. The firm assesses potential not just through exam performance, but considers results alongside strengths, motivations and how applicants align with the firm's values and ambitions.

With exposure to clients early on in their careers, graduates will take on real responsibility and benefit from the knowledge and experience of colleagues. The open and accessible culture gives trainees amazing opportunities to interact with senior business figures, and with support from managers and exceptional training opportunities, they will do everything possible to help build the foundations for a great professional career.

Grant Thornton also offers summer internships and 12-month placements to university students in their penultimate year of study and for those on sandwich-year courses. Both programmes provide a fantastic opportunity to find out more about careers in professional services and life at the firm, and they can offer a fast-track to a Grant Thornton graduate programme.

Once qualified, the opportunities for trainees open up even further. They can continue progressing within their team, explore different business areas or even travel abroad and work at one of the 140+ Grant Thornton member firms around world.

GRADUATE VACANCIES IN 2025

- ACCOUNTANCY
- CONSULTING
- FINANCE

NUMBER OF VACANCIES

350-400 graduate jobs

LOCATIONS OF VACANCIES

STARTING SALARY FOR 2025

£Competitive

WORK EXPERIENCE

DEGREE PLACEMENTS | SUMMER INTERNSHIPS

UNIVERSITY PROMOTIONS DURING 2024-2025

Please check with your university careers service for full details of Grant Thornton's local promotions and events.

APPLICATION DEADLINE

Year-round recruitment

FURTHER INFORMATION

www.Top100GraduateEmployers.com

Register now for the latest news, local promotions, work experience and graduate vacancies at ***Grant Thornton.***

Great minds.
Nothing alike.
If they were, we wouldn't be where we are today. Difference of opinion is something we celebrate, and we'll back you so you can back yourself. Freeing up your time and energy to unlock ideas and innovations that propel our clients, and your career, forward. We value your potential as much as your academic achievements. It's how it should be.
Audit | Tax | Advisory
Visit trainees.grantthornton.co.uk to learn more
Grant Thornton

GSK

gsk.com/en-gb/careers/early-talent

UK.EarlyCareers@gsk.com

GSK   linkedin.com/company/GSK

@GSK   @GSK   youtube.com/GSK

GSK is a global biopharma company strengthened by the belief that getting ahead of disease together – helping prevent disease as well as treating it – is one of the greatest, and most inspiring, challenges there is. By the end of 2030, GSK aims to positively impact the health of 2.5 billion people around the world.

GSK's graduate programmes and direct entry roles offer a unique opportunity to embark on a journey of professional and personal growth. Through real-world experience, graduates will be challenged and supported to develop critical skills that are essential for success in their chosen business area. There are a wide range of options across business operations, manufacturing & supply, research & development, sales, and marketing. Graduates can immerse themselves in their chosen area of expertise while also gaining insights into the diverse operations that drive GSK's global business.

A placement at GSK is an opportunity to take on a role with genuine impact before returning to the final year of university study. They have over 250 placements offering challenging, serious work on live projects or assignments. GSK gets the benefit of new perspectives and fresh thinking. Students get to learn from industry experts, develop their skills and gain valuable experience for wherever the future takes them.

Through its early careers programmes, GSK is committed to helping students and graduates thrive. Managers will engage in open and honest discussions about participants' progress and future. Students and graduates will have access to a multitude of development opportunities through training, mentorship and coaching to support their growth and career progression. They'll have the chance to work alongside industry experts, gaining invaluable hands-on experience and making meaningful contributions to projects that truly make a difference.

GRADUATE VACANCIES IN 2025

- ENGINEERING
- FINANCE
- GENERAL MANAGEMENT
- LOGISTICS
- MARKETING
- PURCHASING
- RESEARCH & DEVELOPMENT
- SALES

NUMBER OF VACANCIES

25+ graduate jobs

LOCATIONS OF VACANCIES

Vacancies also available in Europe, the USA, Asia and elsewhere in the world.

STARTING SALARY FOR 2025

£32,100+

WORK EXPERIENCE

DEGREE PLACEMENTS | SUMMER INTERNSHIPS

UNIVERSITY PROMOTIONS DURING 2024-2025

ASTON, BIRMINGHAM, BRUNEL, DE MONTFORT, GREENWICH, HERTFORDSHIRE, KINGSTON, LANCASTER, NEWCASTLE, QUEEN MARY LONDON

Please check with your university careers service for full details of GSK's local promotions and events.

MINIMUM ENTRY REQUIREMENTS

Relevant degree required for some roles.

APPLICATION DEADLINE

Mid-October - End of October 2024

FURTHER INFORMATION

www.Top100GraduateEmployers.com

Register now for the latest news, local promotions, work experience and graduate vacancies at GSK.

Hogan Lovells

graduates.hoganlovells.com

graduate.recruitment@hoganlovells.com

linkedin.com/company/hoganlovells

@HoganLovellsGradsUK youtube.com/@HoganLovells

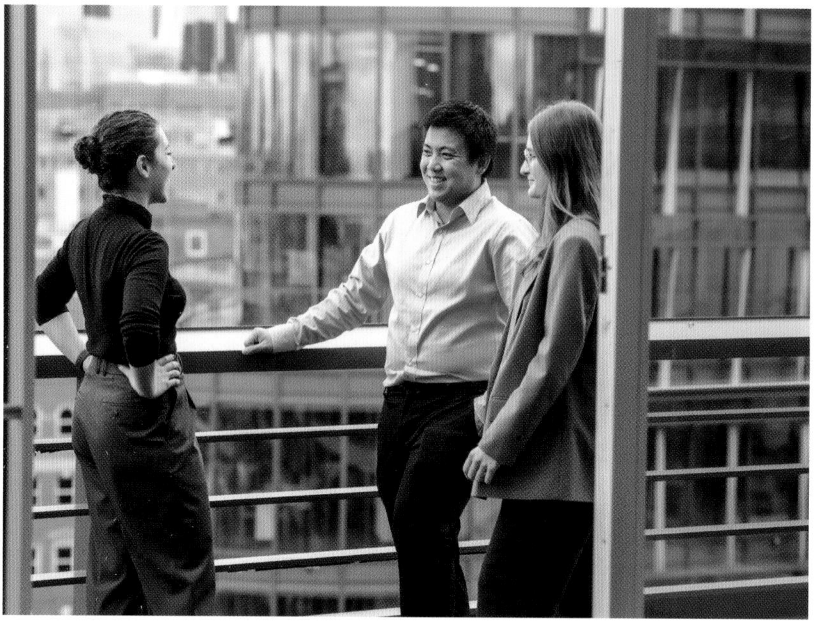

With the combined talent of 2,800+ lawyers spanning six continents and 51 offices, Hogan Lovells bring a world of relevant experience to every matter. They empower people to make innovative choices that drive progress, and make meaningful contributions to clients and society.

Hogan Lovells understand that finding the right firm is one of the most important decisions graduates make at the start of their legal careers. This is why they continue to offer opportunities to students looking to get to know the firm. From vacation schemes to insight events, law fairs, webinars, workshops, and more, all their opportunities are packed with insight and practical experience. Students will meet Hogan Lovells lawyers, delve into broad practice groups and high-profile projects, develop their own commercial awareness, and learn more about the role of a trainee solicitor.

The firm's two-year training contract focuses on practical hands-on learning guided by experienced colleagues. Trainees develop a deep understanding of Hogan Lovells' bold and distinctive approach to collaborating to create valuable global solutions, as they learn from a diverse network of industry leading lawyers. Graduates do four six-month seats across different practice groups – corporate and finance, global regulatory and intellectual property, media and technology, litigation arbitration, and employment. Plus, for one of those seats, they will have the chance to apply for an international or client secondment.

Regardless of their background or chosen path, Hogan Lovells provide graduates with opportunities to grow their legal acumen, sharpen their commercial edge, and tackle real challenges presented by major global clients. With support and encouragement at every stage, Hogan Lovells provide an exceptional platform for graduates to build skills for now and their future.

GRADUATE VACANCIES IN 2025

LAW

NUMBER OF VACANCIES

50 graduate jobs

For training contracts starting in 2027/2028.

LOCATIONS OF VACANCIES

STARTING SALARY FOR 2025

£56,000

WORK EXPERIENCE

INSIGHT COURSES | SEASONAL INTERNSHIPS

UNIVERSITY PROMOTIONS DURING 2024-2025

ABERDEEN, BIRMINGHAM, BRISTOL, CAMBRIDGE, DURHAM, EXETER, KENT, KING'S COLLEGE LONDON, LEICESTER, LSE, NOTTINGHAM, OXFORD, QUEEN MARY LONDON, SOAS LONDON, SURREY, UNIVERSITY COLLEGE LONDON, WARWICK

Please check with your university careers service for full details of Hogan Lovells's local promotions and events.

MINIMUM ENTRY REQUIREMENTS

2.1 Degree

APPLICATION DEADLINE

Year-round recruitment

FURTHER INFORMATION

www.Top100GraduateEmployers.com

Register now for the latest news, local promotions, work experience and graduate vacancies at ***Hogan Lovells.***

HSBC

hsbc.com/earlycareers

uk.graduaterecruitment@hsbc.com

HSBCCareers linkedin.com/company/hsbc

@lifeatHSBC youtube.com/lifeatHSBC

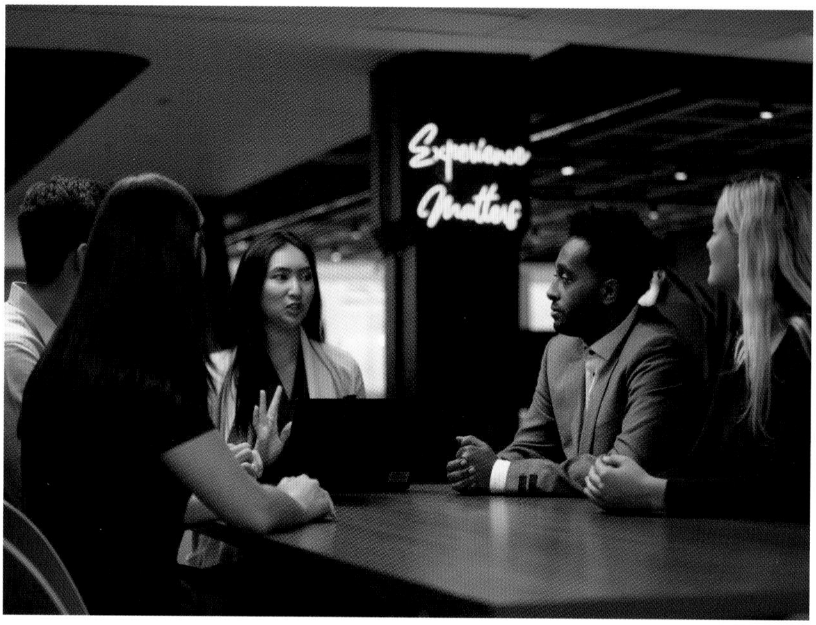

With a global network across 62 countries and territories, serving around 42 million customers, HSBC is one of the world's largest and most connected banking and financial services organisations. Their purpose is focused on opening up a world of opportunity.

HSBC welcomes graduates who bring fresh perspectives and knowledge to the different global businesses and functions. Their graduate programmes are designed to stretch and challenge participants, while providing the skills and experience needed to progress their careers and contribute to HSBC's continuing success. An internship at HSBC offers first-hand experience of what it's like to work for a global bank. Whether in their first, penultimate or final year of undergraduate or postgraduate studies, HSBC offers a wide range of options.

Students and graduates can apply to join HSBC's local or global graduate and internship programmes in the following areas: Commercial Banking, Global Banking & Markets, Wealth and Personal Banking (including Global Asset Management and Private Banking), Digital Business Services, including Operations and Technology.

HSBC programmes are designed to promote continuous learning, networking opportunities and offer insights from across the business. Each global graduate programme begins with an induction, where new joiners will meet one another and their programme managers. Global graduate programmes may include a number of rotations, providing a breadth of experience across the core business areas. Regardless of what subject they studied, HSBC will provide all the necessary tools for success. Structured classroom training, online training and access to the global HSBC University means graduates will constantly update and build their expertise throughout their career at HSBC.

GRADUATE VACANCIES IN 2025

- FINANCE
- GENERAL MANAGEMENT
- INVESTMENT BANKING
- TECHNOLOGY

NUMBER OF VACANCIES

600+ graduate jobs

LOCATIONS OF VACANCIES

Vacancies also available in Europe, the USA, Asia and elsewhere in the world.

STARTING SALARY FOR 2025

£Competitive

Plus bonuses.

WORK EXPERIENCE

INSIGHT COURSES | DEGREE PLACEMENTS | SUMMER INTERNSHIPS

UNIVERSITY PROMOTIONS DURING 2024-2025

ASTON, BIRMINGHAM, CAMBRIDGE, COVENTRY, IMPERIAL COLLEGE LONDON, KING'S COLLEGE LONDON, LEEDS, MANCHESTER, NEWCASTLE, OXFORD, QUEEN MARY LONDON, SHEFFIELD, SHEFFIELD HALLAM, UNIVERSITY COLLEGE LONDON, WARWICK, YORK

Please check with your university careers service for full details of HSBC's local promotions and events.

MINIMUM ENTRY REQUIREMENTS

2.1 Degree

Relevant degree required for some roles.

APPLICATION DEADLINE

November - December 2024

Please see website for full details.

FURTHER INFORMATION

www.Top100GraduateEmployers.com

*Register now for the latest news, local promotions, work experience and graduate vacancies at **HSBC**.*

What does a future leader look like
today?
We're building a bank that's fit for the future, now. It's why we welcome applications to our Global Internships and Graduate Programmes from students and graduates with any degree, from any background.
hsbc.com/earlycareers
HSBC

IBM

ibm.biz/graduate

@LifeAtIBM linkedin.com/company/ibm

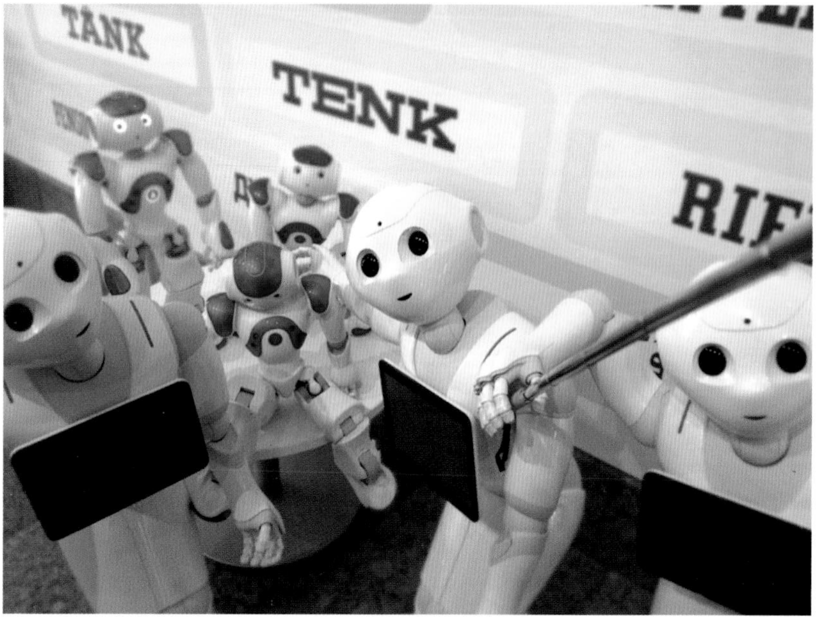

With operations in over 170 countries, IBM is one of the world's largest technology and consulting firms. They're at the forefront of groundbreaking change – improving businesses, society and the human condition. This all starts with their employees, who help provide a new outlook on the world and its emerging tech.

IBM's graduate scheme will give graduates everything they need to build the kind of career they want. With graduate salaries starting at £32,000, a flexible benefits package and opportunities in consulting, technology and design, they will work on challenging projects, have real responsibility, and have access to world class opportunities. They'll be able to collaborate with people who are open-minded and excited about the same things they are.

IBM are looking for enthusiastic, driven and innovative individuals from any degree background. For the company's graduate schemes, applicants will have needed to achieve a 2:1 or higher in any degree discipline. IBM's most successful graduates share a distinct set of characteristics. These begin with energy and creativity, along with a clear focus on delivering exceptional customer service. IBM look for eight specific competencies during the application process: adaptability, communication, client focus, creative problem solving, teamwork, passion for IBM and taking ownership. If potential applicants love working with people and they thrive in a collaborative culture, then they'll fit right in.

Skills development is key to an IBMer's success. To further enhance their professional development, there are opportunities for coaching and mentoring, and graduates will even get a dedicated manager. They will have the opportunity to apply their knowledge in a commercial environment, via on-the-job training, adding value to IBM and its clients.

GRADUATE VACANCIES IN 2025

CONSULTING

TECHNOLOGY

NUMBER OF VACANCIES

150+ graduate jobs

LOCATIONS OF VACANCIES

STARTING SALARY FOR 2025

£34,000

UNIVERSITY PROMOTIONS DURING 2024-2025

ABERYSTWYTH, ASTON, BATH, BIRMINGHAM, BRADFORD, BRISTOL, BRUNEL, CARDIFF, DURHAM, EXETER, IMPERIAL COLLEGE LONDON, KING'S COLLEGE LONDON, LEEDS, LEICESTER, LIVERPOOL, LOUGHBOROUGH, MANCHESTER, NOTTINGHAM, NOTTINGHAM TRENT, OXFORD, OXFORD BROOKES, READING, SOUTHAMPTON, SURREY, UNIVERSITY COLLEGE LONDON, WARWICK

Please check with your university careers service for full details of IBM's local promotions and events.

MINIMUM ENTRY REQUIREMENTS

2.1 Degree

APPLICATION DEADLINE

Please see website for full details.

FURTHER INFORMATION

www.Top100GraduateEmployers.com

Register now for the latest news, local promotions, work experience and graduate vacancies at IBM.

CAREERS AT
MI5
SIS
GCHQ

mi5.gov.uk/careers
sis.gov.uk/explore-careers.html
gchq-careers.co.uk/our-careers.html
linkedin.com/company/careers-at-mi5-sis-and-gchq

The UK's Intelligence Services work together to protect the country's people, businesses and interests. MI5 focuses on security at home, collecting intelligence to mitigate risks. MI6 works worldwide to tackle overseas threats. And GCHQ uses analysis and cyber skills to keep the country safe in the real world and online.

Protecting national security takes a lot of different skills. As a result, there are opportunities for graduates in four unique areas: intelligence, STEM, languages and corporate services. Graduates can train to become an Intelligence Officer at MI5 or MI6. Or if they're interested in analysis, they could become an Intelligence Data Analyst with MI5 or GCHQ. Those passionate about science, technology, engineering or maths, might consider the Technology Graduate Development Programme with MI5 or MI6. Whilst students studying maths can join GCHQ as a maths and cryptography specialist. For linguists, there are exciting opportunities across all three agencies. The most common languages recruited for are Mandarin, Russian, Arabic and Persian. Additionally, there are roles in the corporate service teams, which provide mission-critical support. These include Admin Officers, Business Support Officers, Project Support Officers, and more.

University students can also apply for internships in intelligence, maths and languages, which take place in the summer and autumn across the different agencies. Careers at the UK's Intelligence Services are unlike anywhere else. Their strong emphasis on continuous learning and development means that successful applicants will have access to mentoring, tailored development plans, opportunities to gain professional qualifications, and more.

And when it comes to the future, there's plenty of flexibility. While successful applicants may start their careers with one agency, curiosity and a willingness to learn or specialise could lead to exciting opportunities at MI5, MI6 or GCHQ.

GRADUATE VACANCIES IN 2025
- ENGINEERING
- FINANCE
- GENERAL MANAGEMENT
- HUMAN RESOURCES
- INTELLIGENCE GATHERING
- TECHNOLOGY

NUMBER OF VACANCIES
500+ graduate jobs

LOCATIONS OF VACANCIES

STARTING SALARY FOR 2025
£31,414+
Dependent on programme.

WORK EXPERIENCE
INSIGHT COURSES | SUMMER INTERNSHIPS

UNIVERSITY PROMOTIONS DURING 2024-2025
Please check with your university careers service for full details of the UK Intelligence Services' local promotions and events.

MINIMUM ENTRY REQUIREMENTS
2.2 Degree
Relevant degree required for some roles.

APPLICATION DEADLINE
Year-round recruitment

FURTHER INFORMATION
www.Top100GraduateEmployers.com
Register now for the latest news, local promotions, work experience and graduate vacancies at the ***UK Intelligence Services.***

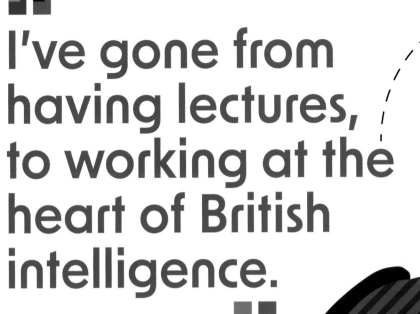

itv

careers.itv.com/teams/early-careers

@ITVCareers ITVCareers

@CareersAtITV linkedin.com/company/itv

ITV is a vertically integrated producer, broadcaster and streamer, consisting of ITV Studios and Media & Entertainment. ITV Studios is a scaled and global creator, owner and distributor of high-quality TV content. It operates in 13 countries, across 60+ labels and has a global distribution network.

ITV's strategic vision is to be a digitally led media and entertainment company that creates and brings its content to audiences wherever, whenever, and however they choose; this is aligned to its purpose to be More than TV.

ITV is the largest free-to-air commercial television network in the UK and is a leading creative force in global content production and distribution, with exciting opportunities for early careers talent.

The Technology Graduate Scheme is a two-year rotational programme working across areas such as software development, data, cyber security and video engineering. In the first year, participants will work within each of the business areas, attend structured training in a development language (Scala, Java or front-end) and do an extended placement with one of the software engineering teams.

A tailored blend of placements, projects and learning opportunities will provide a rounded foundation for a career in media technology and set participants up for a long-lasting career at ITV. They are looking for dynamic and driven people with an appetite for learning. Applicants may have, or be working towards, a science, maths or engineering degree, or have relevant suitable experience.

The ITV Academy offers a range of apprenticeships, traineeship schemes and programmes across the business and in different ITV locations over the country. These serve as entry-level pathways or are open to their own staff, ensuring further development and training is always available. There are also corporate roles in HR, finance, legal, marketing, comms and more.

GRADUATE VACANCIES IN 2025

- ACCOUNTANCY
- FINANCE
- GENERAL MANAGEMENT
- HUMAN RESOURCES
- LAW
- MARKETING
- MEDIA
- RESEARCH & DEVELOPMENT
- SALES
- TECHNOLOGY

NUMBER OF VACANCIES

No fixed quota

LOCATIONS OF VACANCIES

STARTING SALARY FOR 2025

£Competitive

Plus an annual bonus.

WORK EXPERIENCE

INSIGHT COURSES | DEGREE PLACEMENTS | SUMMER INTERNSHIPS

UNIVERSITY PROMOTIONS DURING 2024-2025

Please check with your university careers service for full details of ITV's local promotions and events.

MINIMUM ENTRY REQUIREMENTS

2.2 Degree

Relevant degree required for some roles.

FURTHER INFORMATION

www.Top100GraduateEmployers.com

Register now for the latest news, local promotions, work experience and graduate vacancies at ITV.

J.P.Morgan

jpmorganchase.com/careers

jpmorgan | linkedin.com/company/jpmorgan | @jpmorgan | @jpmorgan | youtube.com/jpmorgan

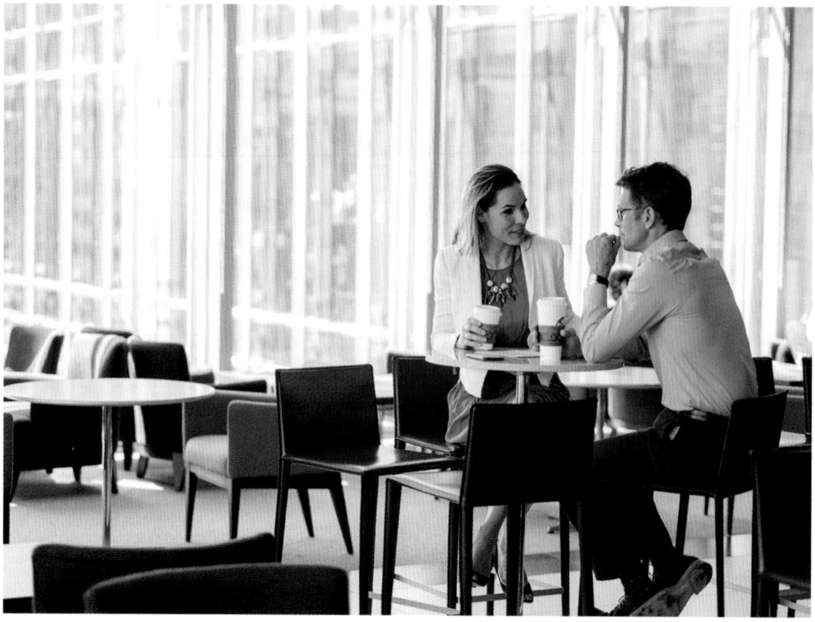

J.P. Morgan is committed to helping businesses and markets grow and develop in more than 100 countries. Over the last 200 years, they have evolved to meet the complex financial needs of some of the world's largest companies, as well as many of the smaller businesses driving industry change.

J.P. Morgan works hard to do the right thing for their clients, shareholders, and the firm every day. Joining the firm means learning from experts in a collaborative team environment where successful applicants will be supported to make an immediate impact from the start. Whilst academic achievements are important, they are looking for individuality and passion, as demonstrated through extra-curricular activities.

J.P. Morgan invest in helping graduates fulfil their potential as they build their career at the firm. Internship and graduate positions are available firmwide, so applicants are encouraged to learn as much as possible about the different business areas and roles. They also offer pre-internship programmes, such as Early Insights, which provide insight into the finance industry and programmes. J.P. Morgan often hire directly from these opportunities – giving successful applicants early exposure to the firm and how they do business.

The internship and full-time programmes they hire into are: asset management, corporate analyst development, data science & machine learning, global finance & business management, human resources, investment banking, markets, quantitative research, risk, software engineer, tech connect, wealth management, wholesale payments, and corporate banking.

Working with a team committed to doing their best, earning the trust of their clients, and encouraging employees to fulfil their potential – that's what it means to be part of J.P. Morgan.

GRADUATE VACANCIES IN 2025

- ACCOUNTANCY
- FINANCE
- HUMAN RESOURCES
- INVESTMENT BANKING
- RESEARCH & DEVELOPMENT
- SALES
- TECHNOLOGY

NUMBER OF VACANCIES
400+ graduate jobs

LOCATIONS OF VACANCIES

Vacancies also available in Europe.

STARTING SALARY FOR 2025
£Competitive

WORK EXPERIENCE

INSIGHT COURSES | DEGREE PLACEMENTS | SUMMER INTERNSHIPS

UNIVERSITY PROMOTIONS DURING 2024-2025

Please check with your university careers service for full details of J.P. Morgan's local promotions and events.

APPLICATION DEADLINE
24th November 2024

FURTHER INFORMATION
www.Top100GraduateEmployers.com
*Register now for the latest news, local promotions, work experience and graduate vacancies at **J.P. Morgan**.*

J.P.Morgan

Find a career that **fits you.**

We're looking for students with varying experience levels, and all degrees and backgrounds to join our diverse, global team.

As a top employer in financial services, J.P. Morgan does much more than manage money. Here, you'll have more chances to continuously innovate, learn and make a positive impact for our clients, customers and communities.

We offer internships in over 15 different business areas as well as Insight Programs to introduce you to the industry and our company.

Explore roles at
Jpmorgan.com/careers

kpmgcareers.co.uk

KPMGRecruitment | graduate@kpmg.co.uk
@KPMGRecruitment | linkedin.com/company/kpmg-advisory
@KPMGUKCareers | youtube.com/@KPMGUKCareers

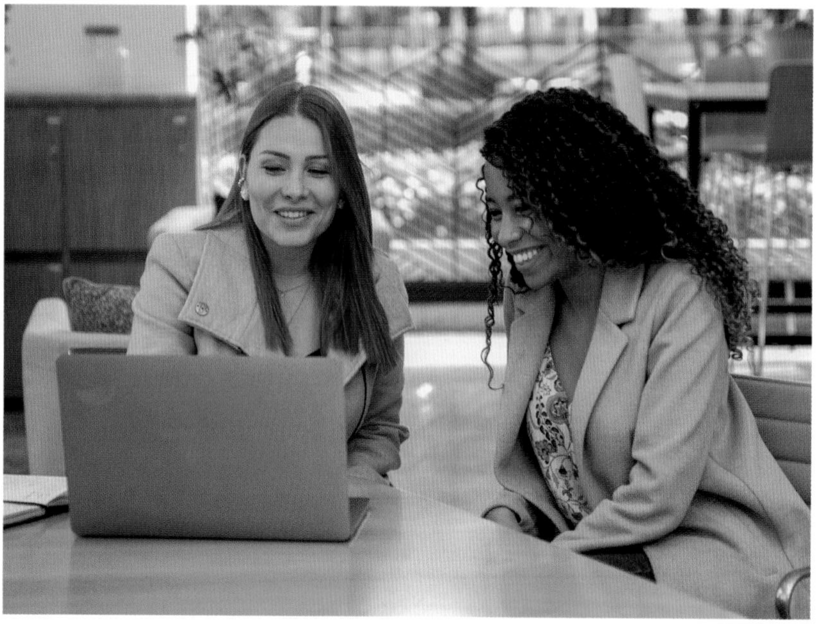

KPMG in the UK is part of a global network of independent firms that offer audit, consulting, deal advisory, tax and law, and technology services. They work with a diverse client base, helping them navigate complex regulatory environments and improve their operational efficiencies to grow and thrive.

KPMG's graduate programmes are designed to build solid foundations in a supportive, collaborative environment, while gaining a professional qualification. Programmes vary in length and are available across audit, consulting, deal advisory, tax and law, and technology and engineering. Audit is KPMG's biggest practice and helps to build trust in businesses and the economy. Across the programmes, graduates will work with clients from day one to transform businesses, find innovative solutions, and gain a deeper understanding of the commercial world. They can also choose to specialise in areas such as climate risk and sustainability, or data analytics.

The undergraduate programmes offered by KPMG provide a rich learning curriculum to help young people explore work at the professional services firm. Participants are supported by their performance manager, training plans, mentorship, and the chance to learn from fellow peers.

In addition, insight programmes are available for students from lower socioeconomic backgrounds, Black Heritage, or students with disabilities. Many of these paid opportunities include a final assessment; guaranteeing participants a place on their chosen programme for the following year. KPMG's inclusivity hopes to welcome graduates to life at the firm as valued members of their community. A career path at KPMG encourages continuous growth, learning and development throughout the graduate programmes, and as participants become confident, experienced professionals in their chosen field.

GRADUATE VACANCIES IN 2025

ACCOUNTANCY
CONSULTING
LAW
TECHNOLOGY

NUMBER OF VACANCIES

1,000 graduate jobs

LOCATIONS OF VACANCIES

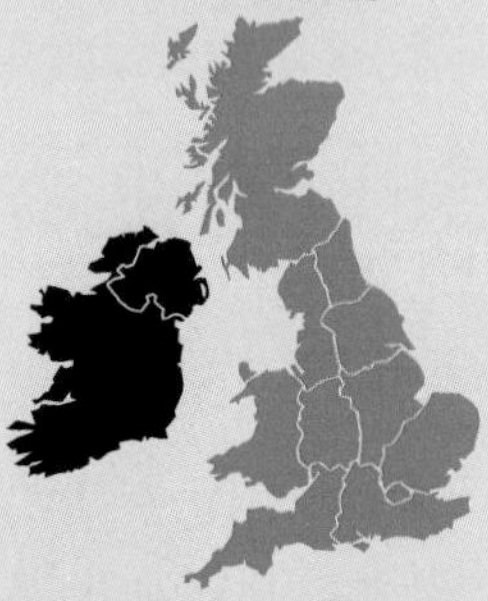

STARTING SALARY FOR 2025

£Competitive

Plus benefits.

WORK EXPERIENCE

DEGREE PLACEMENTS | SUMMER INTERNSHIPS

UNIVERSITY PROMOTIONS DURING 2024-2025

ABERDEEN, ASTON, BIRMINGHAM, BRIGHTON, BRISTOL, BRUNEL, CARDIFF, CITY, COVENTRY, ESSEX, GLASGOW, GLASGOW CALEDONIAN, HERIOT-WATT, KING'S COLLEGE LONDON, LEEDS, LIVERPOOL JOHN MOORES, MANCHESTER, NEWCASTLE, NORTHUMBRIA, NOTTINGHAM, NOTTINGHAM TRENT, PLYMOUTH, PORTSMOUTH, QUEEN MARY LONDON, READING, ROBERT GORDON, ROYAL HOLLOWAY LONDON, SHEFFIELD HALLAM, SOUTHAMPTON, STIRLING, STRATHCLYDE, SURREY, SWANSEA, UEA

MINIMUM ENTRY REQUIREMENTS

2.1 Degree

APPLICATION DEADLINE

Year-round recruitment

FURTHER INFORMATION

www.Top100GraduateEmployers.com

Register now for the latest news, local promotions, work experience and graduate vacancies at KPMG.

L'ORÉAL
UK & IRELAND

careers.loreal.com/en_US/content/UK

lorealgroupe | earlycareersrecruitmentuki@loreal.com
@lorealgroupe | linkedin.com/company/loréal
@lorealgroupe | youtube.com/loreal | @lorealgroupe

L'Oréal is the world's number one beauty company, with a portfolio of 36 international brands. Their goal is to offer each and every person around the world the best of beauty in terms of quality, efficacy, safety, sincerity, and responsibility, to satisfy all beauty needs and desires in their infinite diversity.

L'Oréal UK & Ireland, the leading player in the multi-billion pound beauty industry in the UK, look for an entrepreneurial mindset in their graduates. They believe in developing their people from the ground up, providing their employees with the opportunity to grow within the company, develop a broad future focused skill set and build a dynamic career. As a result, a portion of graduate roles are filled by talents from their Internship and Spring Insights Programs, creating a future focused early careers journey at L'Oréal.

The remainder of the graduate roles are sourced from the external market, to ensure an equal opportunity for all candidates to join this exciting business. On the Management Trainee Program, they will work in different functions and brands across the business, gaining multiple perspectives of life at L'Oréal.

With three different rotations in their chosen stream, graduates are free to develop their strengths and discover new possibilities, shaping their future career as they go. With development programmes and their own mentor, graduates will progress into operational roles in as little as 18 months.

L'Oréal is committed to being one of the top employers in the UK, fostering a workplace where everyone feels welcomed and valued. Promoting gender equality, driving diversity and inclusion, addressing mental health, and establishing evolving workplace practices are a key focus. Through 'L'Oréal for the Future', L'Oréal's global sustainability programme, the business is driving change across all areas including product design, supply chain and consumer behaviour.

GRADUATE VACANCIES IN 2025
- FINANCE
- HUMAN RESOURCES
- LOGISTICS
- MARKETING
- PURCHASING
- SALES

NUMBER OF VACANCIES
40-50 graduate jobs

LOCATIONS OF VACANCIES

STARTING SALARY FOR 2025
£35,000

WORK EXPERIENCE
INSIGHT COURSES | DEGREE PLACEMENTS | SUMMER INTERNSHIPS

UNIVERSITY PROMOTIONS DURING 2024-2025
BATH, CAMBRIDGE, DURHAM, EXETER, IMPERIAL COLLEGE LONDON, LEEDS, LOUGHBOROUGH, LSE, MANCHESTER, NOTTINGHAM, NOTTINGHAM TRENT, OXFORD, UNIVERSITY COLLEGE LONDON, WARWICK
Please check with your university careers service for full details of L'Oréal's local promotions and events.

APPLICATION DEADLINE
October 2024 - February 2025

FURTHER INFORMATION
www.Top100GraduateEmployers.com
*Register now for the latest news, local promotions, work experience and graduate vacancies at **L'Oréal**.*

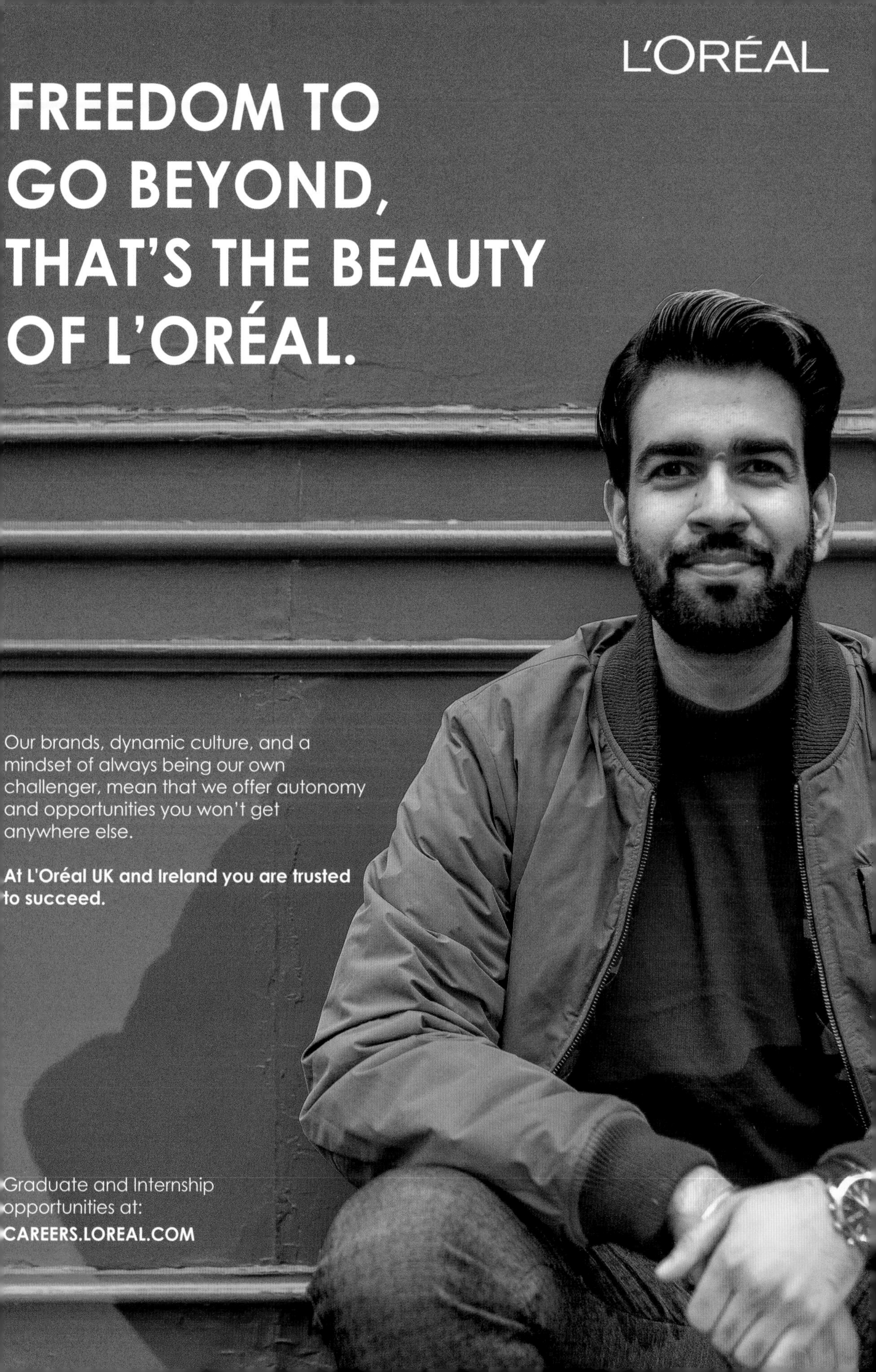
L'ORÉAL
FREEDOM TO GO BEYOND, THAT'S THE BEAUTY OF L'ORÉAL.
Our brands, dynamic culture, and a mindset of always being our own challenger, mean that we offer autonomy and opportunities you won't get anywhere else.
At L'Oréal UK and Ireland you are trusted to succeed.
Graduate and Internship opportunities at:
CAREERS.LOREAL.COM

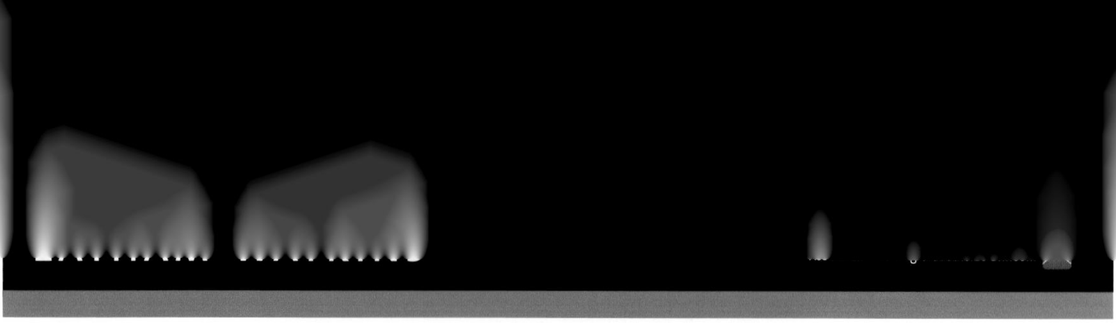

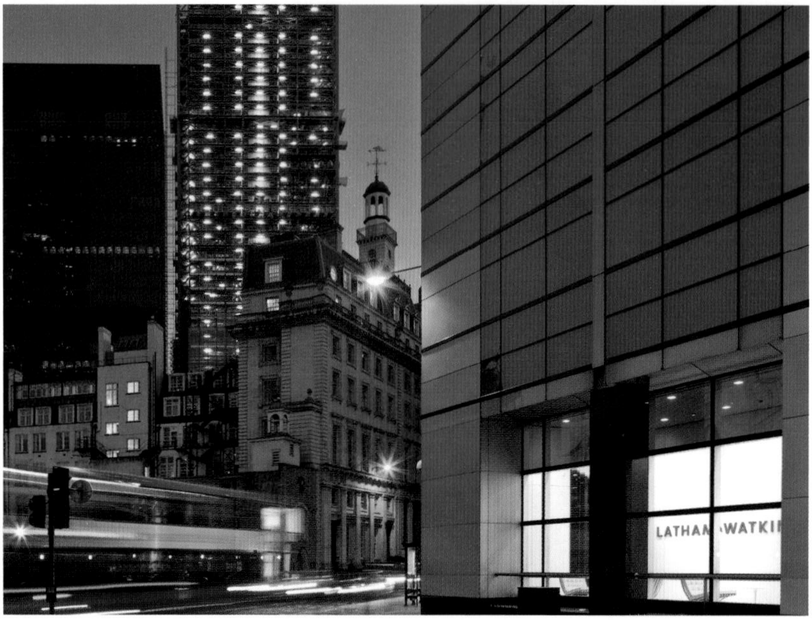

Latham & Watkins is one of the world's largest law firms, with more than 3,000 lawyers in offices across Europe, the US, the Middle East, and Asia. The firm is a global leader in corporate transactions, environmental law, finance matters, litigations and trials, and tax services.

Latham & Watkins runs two vacation schemes over the academic year for applicants to get to know the firm and get a taste of life as a trainee lawyer. Over the course of the scheme, participants will gain insight into two practice areas, participating in client calls, court visits, Q&As and training sessions, as well as group work and social events. These schemes equip participants with a better sense of the kind of lawyer they want to be, after which they will have the opportunity to interview for a training contract.

The two-year training contract combines real responsibility on global matters, with supervision from world-class lawyers who foster professional development. In addition to a sophisticated training programme, trainees also benefit from a core two-week trainee foundation designed to bridge the gap between law schools and practice, as well as training in each seat. After induction, trainees complete four, six month seats – two of which will be in corporate and finance. Trainees have the opportunity to apply for an international secondment on either the third or fourth seat.

Latham & Watkins also offers a work experience programme for Year 12 & 13 students through its partnership with PRIME. More information on the eligibility criteria can be found on their early careers website.

Across all programmes, the firm offers exceptional training and support to ensure seamless collaboration on projects that span time zones, teams, and offices in the world's major financial, business, and regulatory centres.

GRADUATE VACANCIES IN 2025

LAW

NUMBER OF VACANCIES

32 graduate jobs

For training contracts starting in 2027.

LOCATIONS OF VACANCIES

STARTING SALARY FOR 2025

£55,000

WORK EXPERIENCE

INSIGHT COURSES | DEGREE PLACEMENTS | SUMMER INTERNSHIPS

UNIVERSITY PROMOTIONS DURING 2024-2025

BATH, BIRMINGHAM, BRISTOL, CAMBRIDGE, DURHAM, EXETER, KENT, KING'S COLLEGE LONDON, LANCASTER, LEEDS, LSE, NOTTINGHAM, OXFORD, QUEEN MARY LONDON, UNIVERSITY COLLEGE LONDON, WARWICK

Please check with your university careers service for full details of Latham & Watkins' local promotions and events.

MINIMUM ENTRY REQUIREMENTS

2.1 Degree

APPLICATION DEADLINE

Please see website for full details.

FURTHER INFORMATION

www.Top100GraduateEmployers.com

*Register now for the latest news, local promotions, work experience and graduate vacancies at **Latham & Watkins**.*

lidlgraduatecareers.co.uk

linkedin.com/company/lidl-gb youtube.com/@lidlgb

Lidl is the game-changing supermarket known for being big on quality, Lidl on price. They have 960+ stores, 14 warehouses, and over 32,000 colleagues nationwide. They're also big on providing the best programmes in the business, giving graduates the opportunity to really make their mark.

Lidl's rotational programme takes graduates on a hands-on learning journey across their core business areas of sales, logistics and supply chain, providing plenty of opportunity to build experience, resilience, and business acumen. Designed with rapid development in mind, the programme equips graduates with all the tools they need to succeed, progress, and make an impact at Lidl. Graduates with a 2:2 degree or above in any discipline can apply if they have graduated within the past two years by September of the application year.

Lidl graduates learn from industry leaders, with each programme uniquely tailored to provide a clear development path through hands-on, structured training. Opportunities are nationwide, and Lidl also have head office graduate opportunities based in Tolworth, Southwest London.

From day one, graduates will build skills and realise their potential as they discover what it takes to be part of a global organisation. From being committed to sustainability, to working with local charities and food redistributors through CSR programmes – Lidl are more than just a discount retailer. They are looking for ambitious, dedicated talent with character and potential to join their graduate programmes; to challenge and change the world of grocery retail, and to become one of Lidl's future leaders.

Lidl provides industry-leading competitive pay and excellent benefits, including 30 days' holiday per year, an in-store discount, and additional discounts on gym memberships, shopping, and much more.

GRADUATE VACANCIES IN 2025

- GENERAL MANAGEMENT
- LOGISTICS
- PURCHASING
- RETAIL

NUMBER OF VACANCIES

30-50 graduate jobs

LOCATIONS OF VACANCIES

STARTING SALARY FOR 2025

£40,000

UNIVERSITY PROMOTIONS DURING 2024-2025

Please check with your university careers service for full details of Lidl's local promotions and events.

MINIMUM ENTRY REQUIREMENTS

2.2 Degree

APPLICATION DEADLINE

October - November 2024

FURTHER INFORMATION

www.Top100GraduateEmployers.com

Register now for the latest news, local promotions, work experience and graduate vacancies at ***Lidl.***

Big ambitions? Big ideas? Big goals?
You're Lidl like us.
Ledor
Seda
Farida
Find your fit at Lidl.
Visit lidlgraduatecareers.co.uk today.

Linklaters

careers.linklaters.com

@LinklatersGraduatesUK
trainee.recruitment@linklaters.com
linkedin.com/company/linklaters
youtube.com/LinklatersCareers

Unlike many law firms, Linklaters has consistent, market-leading global teams across the full range of practice areas within corporate law. Wherever their lawyers focus, they are involved in the most interesting and dynamic work. Linklaters provides its people with the opportunity to shape their careers from day one.

With 31 offices across 21 countries, Linklaters lawyers act for the world's leading corporates, banks, funds, governments and non-profit organisations on their most complex and challenging assignments. As a truly global business, they solve unique problems and provide exceptional development opportunities.

When people join Linklaters, they find colleagues they want to work with in a truly high performance culture. Linklaters has inspiring and personable professionals who are generous with their time and always happy to help. Their success is built on working together and they look for individuals who will collaborate and innovate to deliver the smartest solutions for clients.

Linklaters recruits candidates from a range of different backgrounds and disciplines, not just law, because those candidates bring with them a set of unique skills and perspectives that can help to challenge conventional thinking and inspire different approaches to client problems.

Over two years, trainees rotate through four seats (placements) in different practice areas, with most trainees going on international or client secondments. Linklaters are committed to providing world-class training and practical experience, alongside support, mentorship and coaching. They offer a fully rounded programme to rapidly develop understanding of commercial law.

Attend an insight event, join a diversity and access programme, participate in a vacation scheme or start as a trainee solicitor, and graduates will find Linklaters offers outstanding, career-long opportunities.

GRADUATE VACANCIES IN 2025

LAW

NUMBER OF VACANCIES

100 graduate jobs

For training contracts starting in 2027.

LOCATIONS OF VACANCIES

STARTING SALARY FOR 2025

£56,000

WORK EXPERIENCE

INSIGHT COURSES | SUMMER INTERNSHIPS

UNIVERSITY PROMOTIONS DURING 2024-2025

ABERDEEN, ASTON, BELFAST, BIRMINGHAM, BRISTOL, CAMBRIDGE, CARDIFF, CITY, DURHAM, EDINBURGH, ESSEX, EXETER, GLASGOW, IMPERIAL COLLEGE LONDON, KING'S COLLEGE LONDON, KENT, LANCASTER, LEEDS, LEICESTER, LONDON SCHOOL OF ECONOMICS, LOUGHBOROUGH, MANCHESTER, NOTTINGHAM, NOTTINGHAM TRENT, OXFORD, OXFORD BROOKES, QUEEN MARY LONDON, SCHOOL OF AFRICAN STUDIES, SHEFFIELD, SOUTHAMPTON, ST ANDREWS, SURREY, SUSSEX, SWANSEA, UEA, UNIVERSITY COLLEGE LONDON, WARWICK, YORK

MINIMUM ENTRY REQUIREMENTS

2.1 Degree

APPLICATION DEADLINE

12th December 2024

FURTHER INFORMATION

www.Top100GraduateEmployers.com

Register now for the latest news, local promotions, work experience and graduate vacancies at ***Linklaters.***

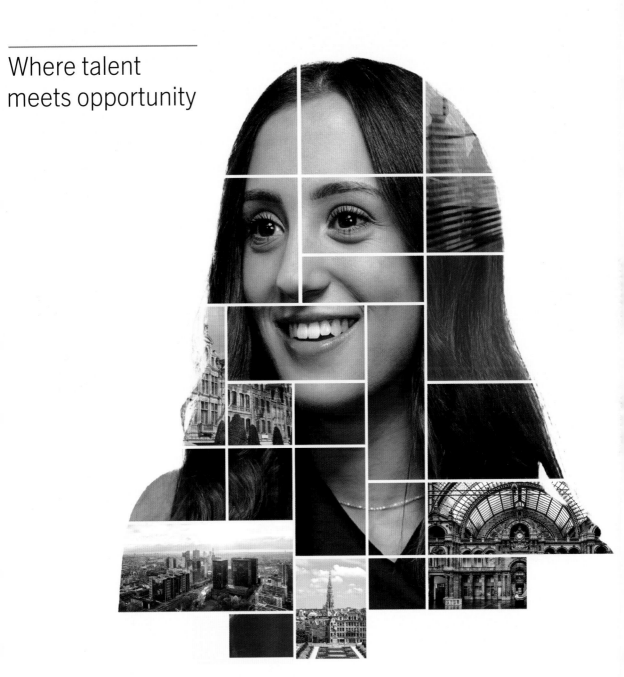

LLOYDS
BANKING GROUP

lloydsbankinggrouptalent.com

lloydsbankinggrouptalent@peoplescout.co.uk
LBGEarlyTalent linkedin.com/company/lloyds-banking-group
LBGEarlyTalent youtube.com/LloydsBankingGroupCareers

With over 26 million customers, Lloyds Banking Group is the largest UK retail and commercial financial services provider. It offers a wide range of opportunities to make a real impact on customers, communities, and the planet, through brands like Lloyds Bank, Halifax, Bank of Scotland and Scottish Widows.

The world is constantly evolving, with new knowledge and technologies impacting how people bank every day. To meet the ever-changing needs of their customers, Lloyds Banking Group is welcoming a new digital future. They invite graduates with a wide range of skills and experience to explore the possibilities of this transformation with them.

The Group is looking for graduates who are excited by rewarding challenges, committed to long-term sustainability, and are inspired by their core purpose of 'Helping Britain Prosper'. Whether it's forming relationships with clients or developing the next generation of technology, graduates will have a significant impact on the journey Lloyds Banking Group is taking.

There are a variety of graduate opportunities available – from software engineering to data science, finance to risk, sustainable financial wellbeing and more. Whichever area graduates choose, they will receive support to achieve professional qualifications and benefit from long-term career progression and development. Graduates will grow in a genuinely inclusive and supportive environment, where learning is central, flexible working is championed, and everyone is free to be themselves. Because Lloyds Banking Group understand that people do their best work when they feel valued, respected and trusted.

A number of internships and vacation schemes are also available for early careers talent so students and graduates can imagine what's next, for their careers, and the future of financial services, at Lloyds Banking Group.

GRADUATE VACANCIES IN 2025
- ACCOUNTANCY
- ENGINEERING
- FINANCE
- HUMAN RESOURCES
- INVESTMENT BANKING
- TECHNOLOGY

NUMBER OF VACANCIES
100+ graduate jobs

LOCATIONS OF VACANCIES

STARTING SALARY FOR 2025
£42,000

WORK EXPERIENCE
INSIGHT COURSES | DEGREE PLACEMENTS | SUMMER INTERNSHIPS

UNIVERSITY PROMOTIONS DURING 2024-2025
ASTON, BATH, BIRMINGHAM, BRISTOL, CAMBRIDGE, CARDIFF, DURHAM, EDINBURGH, GLASGOW, KING'S COLLEGE LONDON, KENT, LANCASTER, LEEDS, LIVERPOOL, LONDON SCHOOL OF ECONOMICS, MANCHESTER, NEWCASTLE, NOTTINGHAM, OXFORD, QUEEN MARY LONDON, SHEFFIELD, SOUTHAMPTON, STRATHCLYDE, UNIVERSITY COLLEGE LONDON, WARWICK, YORK

MINIMUM ENTRY REQUIREMENTS
2.2 Degree

APPLICATION DEADLINE
Please see website for full details.

FURTHER INFORMATION
www.Top100GraduateEmployers.com
*Register now for the latest news, local promotions, work experience and graduate vacancies at **Lloyds Banking Group**.*

M&S

jobs.marksandspencer.com/early-careers

@LifeatMandS X lifeatmands f

@lifeatmands linkedin.com/company/marks-and-spencer in

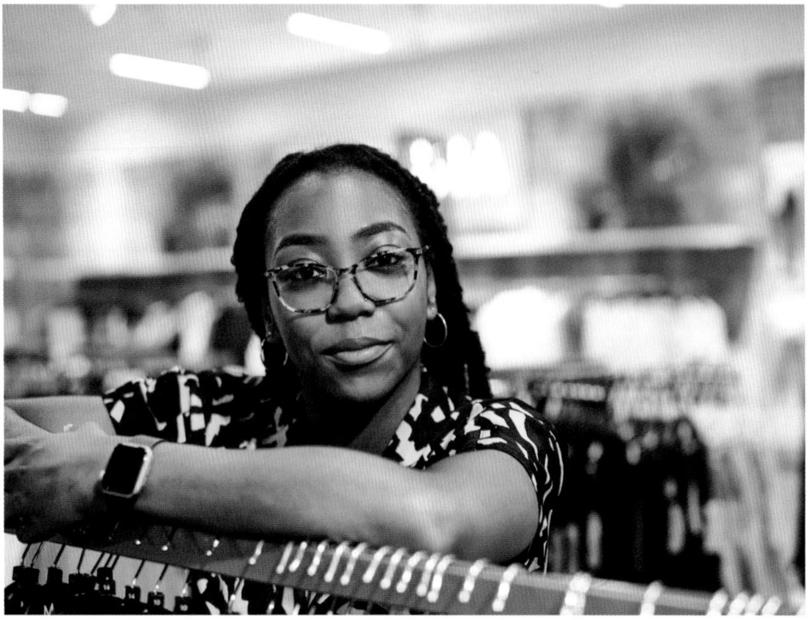

M&S are dedicated to being a trusted retailer, prioritising quality and delivering value. For over a century, they've set the standard. Today, with over 65,000 colleagues serving 32 million customers globally, they continue to put quality products at the heart of everything they do.

M&S are leading the biggest transformation in its history. They are pioneering digital innovation and shaping the future of retail where their values drive every action.

For graduates seeking responsibility from day one, M&S programmes will give them the chance to be bold in a fast-paced environment. Whether it's crafting unique products or leading stores, they will have access to all areas of the business.

M&S have simplified the strategy for their graduate programmes, focusing on three key areas of the business – retail, food, and clothing & home. All graduates start their careers with a placement in-store, where they will engage closely with customers, gain hands-on experience with the products, and learn what it takes to run a successful retail business. Retail vacancies are based across the UK, while the clothing & home and food programmes are predominantly based in their London support centre.

Nurturing graduate talent is a priority for M&S. The company provides structured programmes with mentoring, on-the-job training, and opportunities to solve real challenges that will help build a long-term career. If graduates demonstrate the potential to progress quickly, M&S will provide them with the tools and opportunities to do so. At the same time, they seek applicants that are driven, passionate and will drive their own development, with the support of M&S behind them.

GRADUATE VACANCIES IN 2025

GENERAL MANAGEMENT

PURCHASING

RETAIL

NUMBER OF VACANCIES

60+ graduate jobs

LOCATIONS OF VACANCIES

STARTING SALARY FOR 2025

£32,000

UNIVERSITY PROMOTIONS DURING 2024-2025

Please check with your university careers service for full details of Marks & Spencer's local promotions and events.

APPLICATION DEADLINE

Please see website for full details.

FURTHER INFORMATION

www.Top100GraduateEmployers.com

*Register now for the latest news, local promotions, work experience and graduate vacancies at **Marks & Spencer**.*

Microsoft

careers.microsoft.com/students

MicrosoftLife
@MicrosoftLife linkedin.com/company/microsoft
@MicrosoftLife youtube.com/WorkingAtMicrosoft

Over the last four decades, Microsoft has helped people and organisations use technology to transform how they work, live, and play. Microsoft enables digital transformation for the era of an intelligent cloud and an intelligent edge, empowering every person and every organisation to achieve more.

Alongside traditional engineering opportunities, Microsoft has a range of internship and graduate roles in project management, sales, marketing, consulting and technology. All graduate hires, regardless of role or title, are enrolled on a customised on-boarding process: the Microsoft Aspire Experience.

During a 2 year period, Aspire graduates are exposed to additional training, tools and connections to help them thrive at Microsoft and maximise their performance and learning. Internships and graduate positions are designed for those who thrive in dynamic environments and enjoy a challenge; who believe that technology has the power to transform the world for better. Whatever a new hire's skill set, Microsoft has positions available that will challenge and develop their current capabilities to help realise their full potential.

Successful candidates will gain valuable experience by working on real projects that drive real impact, while being exposed to some of the brightest minds in the industry. Over the course of the programme, they will work alongside other Aspire graduates to build a rich network of connections in over 60 countries.

Microsoft does not just value difference, they seek it out and invite it in. They bring together people from across the globe and support them with employee networks and resource groups to accelerate their professional development and help build a long-term career. Play a vital part in the success of a high-tech global leader. Start a Microsoft journey now.

GRADUATE VACANCIES IN 2025
CONSULTING
MARKETING
SALES
TECHNOLOGY

NUMBER OF VACANCIES
No fixed quota

LOCATIONS OF VACANCIES

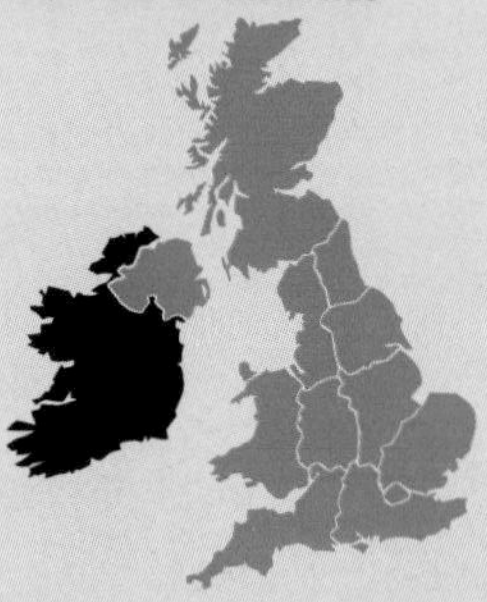

STARTING SALARY FOR 2025
£Competitive
Plus benefits.

WORK EXPERIENCE
DEGREE PLACEMENTS

UNIVERSITY PROMOTIONS DURING 2024-2025
Please check with your university careers service for full details of Microsoft's local promotions and events.

MINIMUM ENTRY REQUIREMENTS
Varies by function
Relevant degree required for some roles.

APPLICATION DEADLINE
February 2025

FURTHER INFORMATION
www.Top100GraduateEmployers.com
*Register now for the latest news, local promotions, work experience and graduate vacancies at **Microsoft**.*

MOTT MACDONALD

mottmac.com/careers/uk-and-ireland-early-careers

earlycareers.recruitment@mottmac.com

@mottmacgroup linkedin.com/company/mott-macdonald

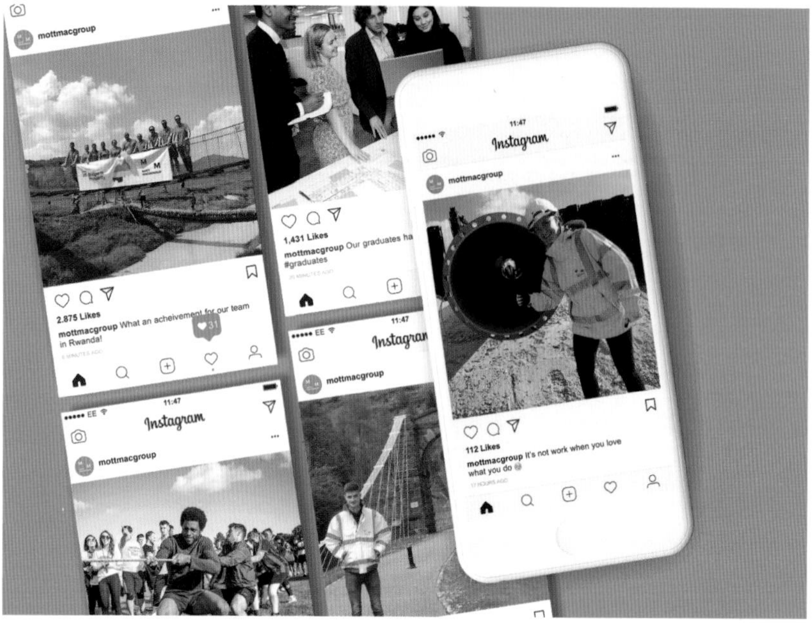

Mott MacDonald is a global engineering, management and development consultancy, delivering projects that create a better future for communities and the world. The company has 20,000 people in over 150 countries, working across areas including transportation, energy, water & environment, advisory, and more.

Students and recent graduates can apply to one of Mott MacDonald's graduate schemes, across all of their business sectors. New graduates will be based in one of the 35 offices in the UK or in mainland Europe.

Mott MacDonald offer summer and year-in-industry placements for students currently pursuing an undergraduate or master's degree. Working on projects alongside graduates and experienced professionals, participants will focus on one of the many sectors and gain valuable experience on community-enhancing projects, learning about the industry and Mott MacDonald as a company. This serves as the perfect springboard onto one of their award-winning graduate career paths, as many of the placement students return to Mott MacDonald after graduating.

All accepted graduates join 'Accelerating Your Future', a three-year development programme that introduces the key business and commercial competencies needed to succeed at Mott MacDonald. Virtual and face-to-face workshops, as well as group challenges, are used to deliver the programme.

Mott MacDonald's early careers paths equip graduates to advance. They will learn from industry experts, receive structured training, and gain experience on community-enhancing projects. Upon joining, graduates are partnered with a mentor who assists with a personalised development plan, and the company provide professional routes that are accredited by organisations such as ICE, IStructE, IMechE, IET, CIBSE, CIWEM, RICS, APM, and more.

GRADUATE VACANCIES IN 2025

CONSULTING

ENGINEERING

NUMBER OF VACANCIES

400 graduate jobs

LOCATIONS OF VACANCIES

Vacancies also available in Europe.

STARTING SALARY FOR 2025

£30,000+

Plus relocation allowance.

WORK EXPERIENCE

DEGREE PLACEMENTS | SUMMER INTERNSHIPS

UNIVERSITY PROMOTIONS DURING 2024-2025

ABERDEEN, ASTON, BATH, BIRMINGHAM, BOURNEMOUTH, BRIGHTON, BRISTOL, CAMBRIDGE, CARDIFF, DURHAM, EDINBURGH, EXETER, HERIOT-WATT, IMPERIAL COLLEGE LONDON, KING'S COLLEGE LONDON, LEEDS, LIVERPOOL, LOUGHBOROUGH, NEWCASTLE, NOTTINGHAM, OXFORD, PLYMOUTH, PORTSMOUTH, QUEEN'S UNIVERSITY, BELFAST, SHEFFIELD, SOUTHAMPTON, STRATHCLYDE, SURREY, SWANSEA, ULSTER, UNIVERSITY COLLEGE LONDON, WARWICK, WEST OF ENGLAND (UWE), YORK

MINIMUM ENTRY REQUIREMENTS

Relevant degree required for some roles.

APPLICATION DEADLINE

Year-round recruitment

FURTHER INFORMATION

www.Top100GraduateEmployers.com

Register now for the latest news, local promotions, work experience and graduate vacancies at Mott MacDonald.

NatWest

jobs.natwestgroup.com

NatWestEarlyCareerRecruitmentTeam@natwest.com

@natwestgroupearlycareers linkedin.com/company/natwest-group

NatWest Group is a leading financial institution operating across the UK with a rich heritage spanning decades. They serve millions of customers and businesses by delivering innovative financial solutions and exceptional service. They are passionate about fostering a diverse and inclusive workplace for their staff.

NatWest Group offer a broad range of graduate programmes in software engineering, data and analytics, and digital transformation – fields that are shaping the future of the financial world – as well as commercial banking, risk, financial crime, and more. These programmes, available across major UK cities, provide hands-on experience, equipping graduates with the skills, knowledge, and practice needed to launch a fulfilling career. Whether applicants are passionate about software development, cyber security, data-driven decision making, protecting customers from financial crime, or sustainability, NatWest has programmes that suit all skill sets and ignite potential.

At NatWest, they believe in 'learning by doing'. As such, their internship programmes in 2025 provide valuable experience across various functions, from human resources to data analytics and financing solutions. The programmes offer support from experienced mentors who guide development, whilst interns gain in-depth experience across the business. Internship positions are open to anyone planning to graduate in 2026.

Supporting growth is a priority for NatWest and their programmes provide opportunities and ongoing learning to keep graduates ahead of the curve. With a supportive environment and a focus on continuous learning, they provide a platform for graduates to unleash their full potential and excel in their chosen field. Whether aspiring to be tech experts, data analysts, or digital innovators, discover the possibilities at NatWest.

GRADUATE VACANCIES IN 2025

- CONSULTING
- FINANCE
- GENERAL MANAGEMENT
- HUMAN RESOURCES
- MARKETING
- TECHNOLOGY

NUMBER OF VACANCIES

250 graduate jobs

LOCATIONS OF VACANCIES

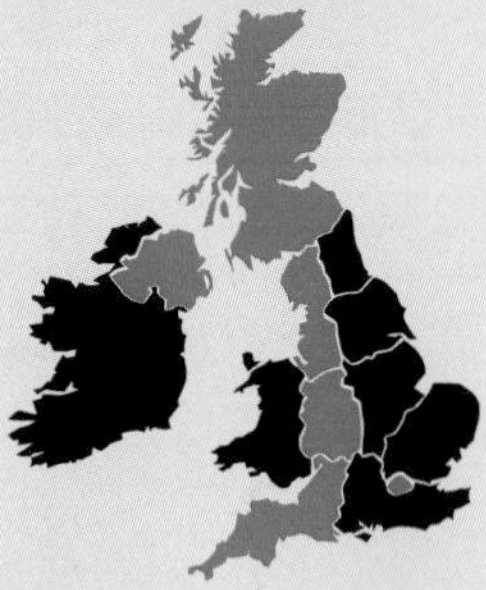

STARTING SALARY FOR 2025

£35,000

WORK EXPERIENCE

INSIGHT COURSES | DEGREE PLACEMENTS | SUMMER INTERNSHIPS

UNIVERSITY PROMOTIONS DURING 2024-2025

ABERDEEN, ASTON, BIRMINGHAM, CITY, DUNDEE, EDINBURGH, EDINBURGH NAPIER, GLASGOW, GREENWICH, HERIOT-WATT, LANCASTER, MANCHESTER, QUEEN MARY LONDON, ST ANDREWS, STRATHCLYDE, WARWICK

Please check with your university careers service for full details of NatWest's local promotions and events.

MINIMUM ENTRY REQUIREMENTS

2.1 Degree

APPLICATION DEADLINE

Year-round recruitment

FURTHER INFORMATION

www.Top100GraduateEmployers.com

*Register now for the latest news, local promotions, work experience and graduate vacancies at **NatWest**.*

NatWest
Group

Nestlé academy
Grow your own future

nestle.co.uk/nestle-academy

@nestleuki linkedin.com/company/nestle-s-a-
@nestleuki youtube.com/NestléUKI

Nestlé is the world's largest food and drink company and is responsible for more than 80 brands in the UK & Ireland. These span categories including confectionery, coffee, cereals, pet care, water, nutrition, food and dairy. Nestlé employs more than 8,000 people in the UK & Ireland across 17 sites including 13 factories.

Nestlé is committed to bringing in new talent and providing a supportive and inclusive environment for everyone to thrive. A place where ideas and innovations can help solve real problems, the opportunity to work with iconic brands in a global company at the forefront of its industry.

Its next intake of graduate schemes, placements, and apprenticeships will go live in November 2024. It offers a wide range of opportunities in different functions and sites across the UK, including HR, sales, supply chain, engineering, technical leadership and more. The graduate schemes last between 2-3 years and offer a starting salary of £32,000. Nestlé also offers financial support for graduates and apprentices who are required to relocate at the start of the scheme. Nestlé recognises that everyone's needs are different and it encourages those applying to come and talk to them about how it can support candidates through the application and assessment process.

Before joining, successful applicants will be able to visit their workplace and get a feel for the culture. People are at the heart of Nestlé, and graduates will be connected with their teams, buddies and other graduates, sharing experiences and offering guidance. Leading experts are ready to share their experience, knowledge and skills; working with graduates to build a professional development plan tailored to individual interests. On the scheme, new joiners will meet with their cohort on graduate weeks, with collaborative sessions designed to provide the space to learn, innovate, solve and inspire!

GRADUATE VACANCIES IN 2025
ENGINEERING
HUMAN RESOURCES
LOGISTICS
MARKETING
RESEARCH & DEVELOPMENT
SALES

NUMBER OF VACANCIES
25-35 graduate jobs

LOCATIONS OF VACANCIES

STARTING SALARY FOR 2025
£32,000

WORK EXPERIENCE
DEGREE PLACEMENTS

UNIVERSITY PROMOTIONS DURING 2024-2025
Please check with your university careers service for full details of Nestlé's local promotions and events.

MINIMUM ENTRY REQUIREMENTS
Relevant degree required for some roles.

APPLICATION DEADLINE
6th January 2025

FURTHER INFORMATION
www.Top100GraduateEmployers.com
Register now for the latest news, local promotions, work experience and graduate vacancies at Nestlé.

Nestlé | **academy**
Grow your own future

@nestleuki @Nestlé
#NestléAcademy

As a graduate at Nestlé, you will emerge with practical skills, industry knowledge and an empowered network. Your ideas and innovations will help solve real problems and you will get to work with iconic brands in a global company at the forefront of its industry.

Starting salary: £32,000
Locations: Across the UK
Duration: 2-3 years
Start date: September 2025

Mentorship: collaborate with experts ready to share their experience, knowledge and skills.

Professional development: tailored to your interests.

Graduate weeks: designed to challenge and help you learn, solve, innovate and inspire.

How do we look after you?

Flexible working options
Pets at work
Relocation support
Comprehensive benefits
Pastoral manager
Employee assistance programme
On site gyms and classes*
Rewards and recognition
Inclusive culture
Wellbeing classes and resources

*Access to facilities vary by site

"I have so much more confidence in my future and where my skills can take me. My advice is to stay curious and ask questions, there will always be someone to help."

Heather Kennedy (she/her)
Sales Graduate

To find out more about the application process and our opportunities, visit **www.nestle.co.uk/nestle-academy** or scan the code below.

Have a question?
Email: Nestle.Academy@uk.nestle.com

newtoneurope.com/careers/graduates

graduates@newtoneurope.com

LifeAtNewton linkedin.com/company/newtonimpact

@lifeatnewton youtube.com/@newton.impact

Newton

Newton is a consultancy that helps organisations realise their strategic ambitions, translating them into real-world outcomes. Specialising in the defence, consumer and public sectors, Newton needs exceptional graduates to create bold, fresh thinking.

The world doesn't stand still and the challenges it faces are always evolving, which is why graduate consultants are encouraged to bring innovative ideas and are empowered to drive change from the start. Newton's clients face some of the most difficult challenges, but the seemingly impossible is where Newton thrives best. Graduates will work hand-in-hand with clients, going as deep as it takes to find answers. It's more than hitting numbers or ticking boxes but delivering meaningful, measurable impact. They have delivered over a £billion in savings for individual clients on more than one occasion.

But what does meaningful impact actually look like? Working with a County Council's Children's Services department, Newton helped reduce the number of children going into residential care from 40 to 17 per year. They have optimised a major railway improvement initiative reducing timelines and improving travel for millions of passengers.

Graduates progress at pace, with no limit to unlocking their potential. Newton is building a community of exceptional people, one built on trust and shared experiences, of challenge and adventure. Collaboration is key, from spending time away on-site to regular whole-company days tackling projects together. Roles are open to applicants from all degree disciplines and can be based anywhere in the UK, as travel to UK-wide project sites is necessary.

Newton brings together exceptional people who will drive development, motivating them to become better versions of themselves.

GRADUATE VACANCIES IN 2025

CONSULTING

NUMBER OF VACANCIES

Around 100 graduate jobs

LOCATIONS OF VACANCIES

STARTING SALARY FOR 2025

£45,000

Plus a £2,500 sign-on bonus and annual profit share. Expected range (realistic) between £2,200-£6,600.

WORK EXPERIENCE

SUMMER INTERNSHIPS

UNIVERSITY PROMOTIONS DURING 2024-2025

BATH, BIRMINGHAM, BRISTOL, CAMBRIDGE, DURHAM, EDINBURGH, EXETER, IMPERIAL COLLEGE LONDON, LSE, MANCHESTER, NOTTINGHAM, OXFORD, SHEFFIELD, ST ANDREWS, STRATHCLYDE, UNIVERSITY COLLEGE LONDON, WARWICK, YORK

Please check with your university careers service for full details of Newton's local promotions and events.

APPLICATION DEADLINE

End of 2024

FURTHER INFORMATION

www.Top100GraduateEmployers.com

Register now for the latest news, local promotions, work experience and graduate vacancies at ***Newton.***

NHS

Graduate Management Training Scheme

graduates.nhs.uk

@NHSGradscheme @NHSGraduatescheme
linkedin.com/company/nhs-graduate-management-training-scheme
youtube.com/NHSGraduateManagementTrainingScheme

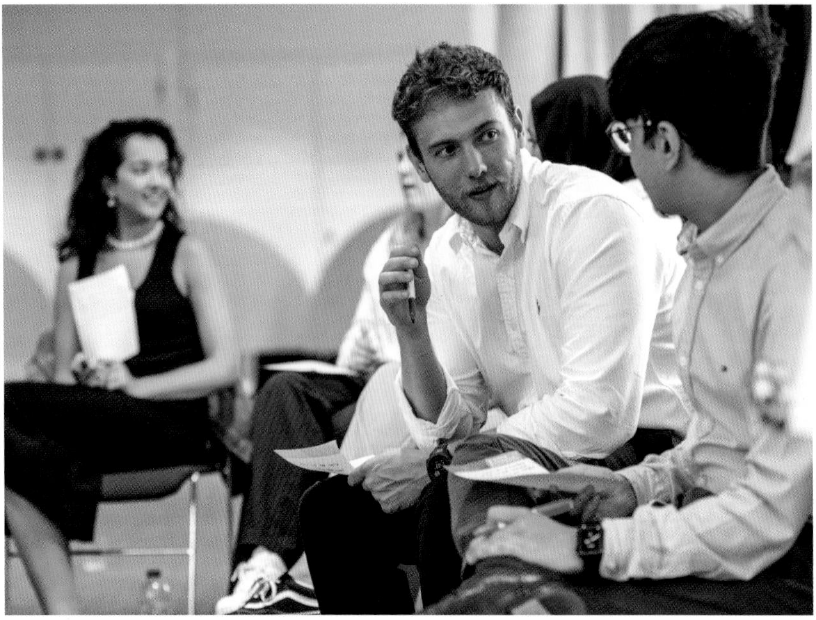

The National Health Service (NHS) is Europe's largest employer, with an annual budget of over £160 billion and a mission to improve the wellbeing of 57 million people. Its Graduate Management Training Scheme (GMTS) is a great place to begin a journey towards becoming a healthcare leader of the future.

GMTS trainees specialise in one of six areas: general management, HR, finance, policy & strategy, health informatics or health analysis. Their work can be in hospital or office settings and can range from A&E data analysis to service improvement, financial planning, and much more. Trainees get access to a comprehensive development package, including on-the-job training within placements where they gain specialist skills and postgraduate qualifications from leading universities. There is a wealth of on-scheme support available which includes pastoral and placement managers and individual support managers.

With just over 200 graduates joining GMTS in 2024, there are many opportunities to build far-reaching networks and learn from fellow peers. The scheme has won multiple awards and gives endless ways to grow personally and professionally, while taking on early leadership responsibility. Graduates are selected based on their leadership potential, values and ambition to make a difference through a management career in health and care.

The NHS offers both great responsibility and development potential. On this fast track to senior leadership, graduates quickly face the exhilarating challenge of handling complex problems and high-profile situations. Facing these challenges, future NHS leaders need the resilience, tenacity and focus to achieve the best results in a compassionate way. Ultimately, it's an incredibly rewarding path where hard work and commitment can affect the lives of millions – and be completely life-changing for graduates themselves.

GRADUATE VACANCIES IN 2025

- ACCOUNTANCY
- FINANCE
- GENERAL MANAGEMENT
- HUMAN RESOURCES
- TECHNOLOGY

NUMBER OF VACANCIES

200 graduate jobs

LOCATIONS OF VACANCIES

STARTING SALARY FOR 2025

£27,702

WORK EXPERIENCE

INSIGHT COURSES | DEGREE PLACEMENTS | SUMMER INTERNSHIPS

UNIVERSITY PROMOTIONS DURING 2024-2025

ASTON, BATH, BIRMINGHAM, BRISTOL, CAMBRIDGE, CITY, ESSEX, EXETER, IMPERIAL COLLEGE LONDON, KING'S COLLEGE LONDON, LEEDS, LEICESTER, LIVERPOOL, LIVERPOOL JOHN MOORES, NOTTINGHAM TRENT, OXFORD, PLYMOUTH, PORTSMOUTH, READING, SOAS LONDON, SOUTHAMPTON, SURREY, UEA, UNIVERSITY COLLEGE LONDON, WEST OF ENGLAND (UWE)

Please check with your university careers service for full details of the NHS's local promotions and events.

MINIMUM ENTRY REQUIREMENTS

2.2 Degree

APPLICATION DEADLINE

31st October 2024

FURTHER INFORMATION

www.Top100GraduateEmployers.com

*Register now for the latest news, local promotions, work experience and graduate vacancies at the **NHS**.*

P&G

pgcareers.com

linkedin.com/showcase/procter-gamble-uk-ireland

@ProcterGamble @proctergamble youtube.com/ProcterGamble

Procter & Gamble (P&G) owns iconic global brands like Gillette, Pampers, Head & Shoulders and Oral-B. With employees from over 140 countries, and operations in approximately 70 countries, P&G aspires to build a better world and enhance the lives of the world's consumers.

As a 'build from within' company, P&G expect those who join at entry level to become their next generation of accomplished leaders. There are no rotational programmes or gradual on-boarding here. Instead, from day one, employees are entrusted with meaningful work that has a tangible impact on P&G's leading brands and their careers. This build-from-within approach means P&G invest heavily in career development with senior leaders supporting graduates to continuously grow their skills and capabilities. Whether helping to design the latest front-end innovation, selling to some of the UK's biggest retailers, or designing a full-blown product launch, P&G employees will be empowered to succeed.

P&G want all their employees to be themselves by creating a culture of acceptance and inclusion for everyone, so they can bring their unique voices to work. They believe in equal voice and representation for all and take their responsibility to build a more equitable world seriously. For example, Gillette's 'Gamechangers' initiative partners with youth education charity Football Beyond Borders to combat racism, and Fairy's #Spreadthelove campaign celebrates Pride and promotes equality.

Joining P&G means being part of an organisation that not only strives for excellence in consumer products but also values making a positive impact on society. With their strong emphasis on leadership development, responsibility from day one, and senior leaders who are invested in supporting the next generation, P&G offers not only a fulfilling career but one where graduates can make an impact right from the start.

GRADUATE VACANCIES IN 2025

- ENGINEERING
- FINANCE
- HUMAN RESOURCES
- LOGISTICS
- MARKETING
- RESEARCH & DEVELOPMENT
- SALES
- TECHNOLOGY

NUMBER OF VACANCIES

100 graduate jobs

LOCATIONS OF VACANCIES

Vacancies also available in Europe.

STARTING SALARY FOR 2025

£40,000

For management graduate roles.
£28,000 for management intern roles.

WORK EXPERIENCE

DEGREE PLACEMENTS | SUMMER INTERNSHIPS

UNIVERSITY PROMOTIONS DURING 2024-2025

BATH, BIRMINGHAM, BRADFORD, BRISTOL, BRUNEL, CAMBRIDGE, DURHAM, EDINBURGH, GLASGOW, HERIOT-WATT, IMPERIAL COLLEGE LONDON, KINGSTON, LEEDS, LIVERPOOL, LOUGHBOROUGH, MANCHESTER, NEWCASTLE, NOTTINGHAM, QUEEN MARY LONDON, SHEFFIELD, STRATHCLYDE, UCL, WARWICK

Please check with your university careers service for full details of P&G's local promotions and events.

MINIMUM ENTRY REQUIREMENTS

Relevant degree required for some roles.

APPLICATION DEADLINE

Please see website for full details.

FURTHER INFORMATION

www.Top100GraduateEmployers.com

Register now for the latest news, local promotions, work experience and graduate vacancies at P&G.

DAY 1.
Gillette
head & shoulders
CLASSIC
CLEAN

penguinrandomhousecareers.co.uk

linkedin.com/company/penguin-random-house-uk

@PenguinUKJobs youtube.com/penguinrandomhouseuknews

Penguin are the UK's largest publisher and their doors are open to all kinds of talent. They want everyone to feel a deep sense of belonging, supported to do their best work and motivated to play a part in realising their shared purpose: to connect more people with great stories and ideas.

Collaboration, creativity, and entrepreneurship lie at the heart of what Penguin do. In a constantly evolving industry, they work hard to stretch the definition of the word publisher. At Penguin, graduates will work with a breadth of talent from editors, technologists, designers, salespeople, publicists, digital marketers, distributors, and many others, to make each of their books a success. Together, Penguin make books for everyone, because a book can change anyone.

Penguin is one of the most widely recognised book publishers in the world, with more than 2,000 people and publishing over 1,500 books each year. Penguin offer a range of vacancies and all that's needed to start a great career. Successful applicants will be supported to make decisions for themselves, and contribute to Penguin's shared mission. Penguin have amazing opportunities, great benefits, and the stability and support to be expected from a big organisation.

Each year Penguin have hundreds of entry level and early-career roles available across their creative book publishing houses and specialist support function teams. Graduates will develop skills through their variety of learning and development training, mentoring, and career pathways.

Find out 'what's next?'. Penguin's emerging talent programmes for those at the start of their career are a great way for graduates to make their mark on a paid traineeship in one of Penguin's welcoming, collaborative and supportive teams.

GRADUATE VACANCIES IN 2025

- ACCOUNTANCY
- FINANCE
- HUMAN RESOURCES
- MARKETING
- MEDIA
- RESEARCH & DEVELOPMENT
- RETAIL
- SALES
- TECHNOLOGY

NUMBER OF VACANCIES

250 graduate jobs

LOCATIONS OF VACANCIES

STARTING SALARY FOR 2025

£27,500-£30,000

WORK EXPERIENCE

INSIGHT COURSES | SUMMER INTERNSHIPS

UNIVERSITY PROMOTIONS DURING 2024-2025

Please check with your university careers service for full details of Penguin's local promotions and events.

APPLICATION DEADLINE

Year-round recruitment

FURTHER INFORMATION

www.Top100GraduateEmployers.com

*Register now for the latest news, local promotions, work experience and graduate vacancies at **Penguin**.*

pfizer.co.uk/careers

Pfizer | studentprogrammesuk@pfizer.com
@Pfizer_News | linkedin.com/company/Pfizer
@PfizerInc | youtube.com/Pfizer

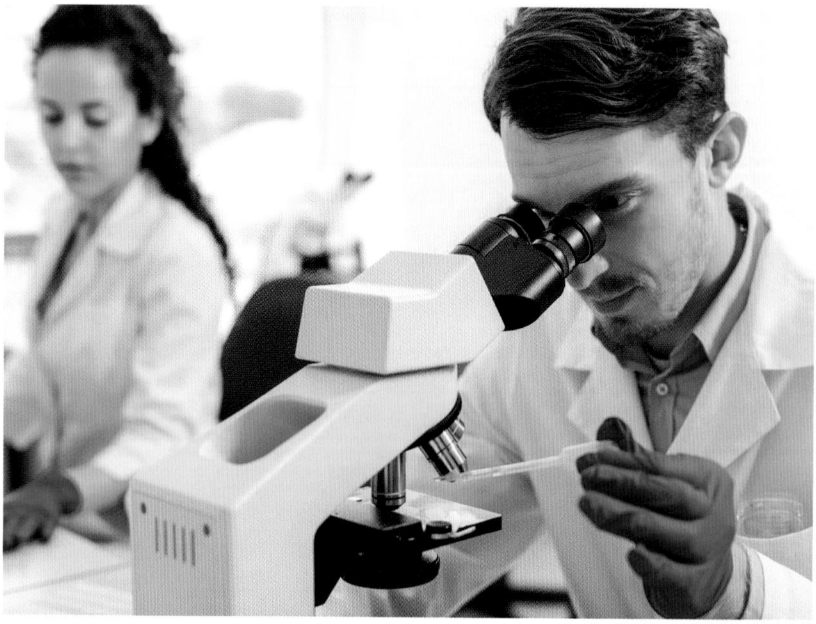

For more than 170 years, Pfizer has worked to make a difference for all. It applies science and global resources to bring therapies to people that extend and significantly improve their lives. Every day, Pfizer colleagues work to advance wellness, prevention, treatments, and cures.

Each year, Pfizer offers up to 100 university undergraduates a 12-month industrial placement, based at one of the company's four UK sites. Whether they join in research & development, commercial, or global operations, placement students will be part of one global team, working to bring vital breakthroughs to patients. They are given a high level of responsibility as they support, manage, and deliver projects in one of the world's most innovative biopharmaceutical companies. During the programme, students will be part of a team that lets them ask questions, share ideas, make discoveries and retain a healthy work-life balance.

Staying true to its values, Pfizer supports its new joiners to gain the courage to run with new ideas and to contribute fully to the success of the team in which they work. It provides undergraduates with a unique set of experiences that will broaden and develop the critical skill sets and competencies they will need to be successful in the business environment and to excel in their degree. Placements are listed on Pfizer's Undergraduate Vacancies webpage from September each year, with new positions added through to December.

Undergraduates who complete a successful 12-month industrial placement can apply for Pfizer UK's Future Leader Graduate Programme; but this isn't the only route available for graduates looking for a career within Pfizer. A number of entry-level roles are available across its UK sites and these opportunities are advertised throughout the year on the Pfizer Careers website.

GRADUATE VACANCIES IN 2025

- ENGINEERING
- FINANCE
- GENERAL MANAGEMENT
- MARKETING
- TECHNOLOGY

NUMBER OF VACANCIES

15-20 graduate jobs

LOCATIONS OF VACANCIES

STARTING SALARY FOR 2025

£27,000-£33,000

WORK EXPERIENCE

DEGREE PLACEMENTS | SUMMER INTERNSHIPS

UNIVERSITY PROMOTIONS DURING 2024-2025

Please check with your university careers service for full details of Pfizer's local promotions and events.

MINIMUM ENTRY REQUIREMENTS

Relevant degree required for some roles.

APPLICATION DEADLINE

Year-round recruitment

FURTHER INFORMATION

www.Top100GraduateEmployers.com

*Register now for the latest news, local promotions, work experience and graduate vacancies at **Pfizer**.*

POLICE:NOW

INFLUENCE FOR GENERATIONS

policenow.org.uk

graduates@policenow.org.uk

PoliceNow linkedin.com/school/police-now

@PoliceNowGraduates youtube.com/PoliceNowChangeTheStory

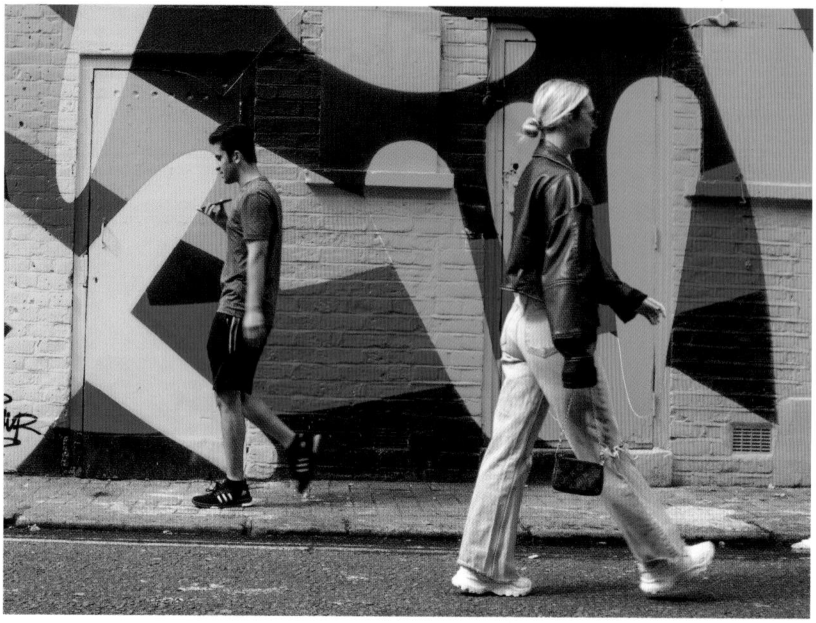

With public trust at an all-time low, policing needs the right officers, right now. It is time for change. For our communities and the most vulnerable – who demand better. Police Now is a charity that transforms communities by recruiting outstanding and diverse graduates to be leaders on the policing frontline.

Police Now offers the only national graduate programmes for policing. Graduates work on big societal issues, help create safer communities and drive a positive and fair internal culture in policing. Graduates get paid a salary from day one while they train to become neighbourhood police officers or police detectives.

The training empowers graduates to make an immediate and real impact on the lives of society's most vulnerable and gain the confidence needed to drive transformative change.

Over two years, graduates develop their problem-solving and leadership skills, beginning with an award-winning training academy, while receiving support from a dedicated Performance and Development Coach to aid their growth.

As part of the National Graduate Leadership Programme, neighbourhood police officers can apply for a four-week secondment. This is a unique opportunity to develop skills and gain valuable experience working with external partners like the Home Office. After successfully completing the two-year programme, graduates become fully warranted officers. Ongoing career and promotion support is provided by Police Now beyond the programme and throughout their policing careers.

Graduates from all degree disciplines have the potential to join a Police Now programme. Few careers offer the combination to make a meaningful difference where it matters most, and a breadth of opportunities for progression.

GRADUATE VACANCIES IN 2025

POLICING

NUMBER OF VACANCIES

400 graduate jobs

LOCATIONS OF VACANCIES

STARTING SALARY FOR 2025

£28,551-£36,775+

Dependent on location.

UNIVERSITY PROMOTIONS DURING 2024-2025

ASTON, BATH, BIRMINGHAM, BRISTOL, CARDIFF, DURHAM, EXETER, LANCASTER, LEEDS, LEICESTER, LIVERPOOL, MANCHESTER, NEWCASTLE, NOTTINGHAM, SHEFFIELD, WARWICK, YORK

Please check with your university careers service for full details of Police Now's local promotions and events.

MINIMUM ENTRY REQUIREMENTS

2.2 Degree

In any discipline.

APPLICATION DEADLINE

Please see website for full details.

FURTHER INFORMATION

www.Top100GraduateEmployers.com

Register now for the latest news, local promotions, work experience and graduate vacancies at ***Police Now.***

CHANGE
THE STORY
What if your actions could change society for the better?
As a neighbourhood police officer, you can stop crime before it happens. You can help communities rocked by injustice. You can build a better tomorrow.
Our two-year programme develops your leadership and problem-solving skills so that you can reduce crime and transform communities.
Join the only national graduate programme for neighbourhood policing.
POLICE:NOW
INFLUENCE FOR GENERATIONS
Scan to read Anokhi's story
or visit
policenow.org.uk
"When looking at how to make an impact in policing, I was pulled towards how I could improve it from the inside."
Anokhi Chouhan | Police Now Graduate
A starting salary of £28,551 - £36,775 depending on location.
A dedicated Performance and Development Coach to support you.
A peer network of over 3,000 Police Now officers.
A secondment opportunity inside or outside of policing in your second year.

pwc

pwc.co.uk/careers

PwCCareersUK
@pwc_uk_careers linkedin.com/company/pwc-uk
@pwc_uk_careers youtube.com/@pwc_uk_careers

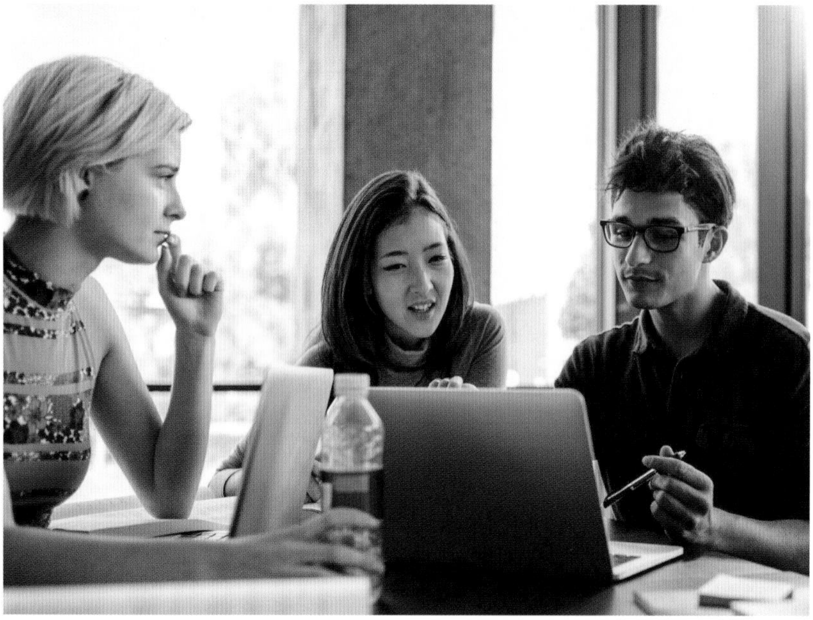

PwC is a global professional services network operating in 151 countries, with 25,000 employees across the UK. They specialise in delivering quality assurance, tax, and advisory services to help organisations and individuals create value and solve important problems.

With 19 offices across the UK, PwC offer graduate opportunities across actuarial, audit, business solutions, consulting, deals, legal, operate, risk, tax, and technology. Roles are open to applicants from all degree disciplines. This is a rewarding career path, equipped with the tools and experiences necessary for long-term success.

In addition, PwC offer a range of undergraduate work placements and summer internships designed for students in their penultimate year of a degree, or final year with a confirmed one-year postgraduate degree. They recruit over 400 paid summer interns each year, across various business areas and locations. Internships begin with a regional induction event, providing insight into PwC's culture, and the chance to network with peers and professionals from across the business. This is followed by on-the-job training, preparing interns to work on client projects. For students required to complete a year in industry as part of their undergraduate degree, PwC offers 11-month paid work placements. Throughout the placement, participants benefit from excellent learning and development opportunities, gaining valuable insights and practical experience.

PwC seeks individuals who are eager to learn, grow, and inspire others. From specialist training courses and toolkits to informal 'lunch and learn' sessions hosted by peers, PwC ensures that learning is continuous and comprehensive. New hires are guided by their teammates and supported by a dedicated career coach who helps navigate career paths and learning objectives.

GRADUATE VACANCIES IN 2025

ACCOUNTANCY
CONSULTING
FINANCE
LAW
TECHNOLOGY

NUMBER OF VACANCIES

1,500+ graduate jobs

LOCATIONS OF VACANCIES

Vacancies also available elsewhere in the world.

STARTING SALARY FOR 2025

£Competitive

Plus an annual bonus plan.

WORK EXPERIENCE

INSIGHT COURSES | DEGREE PLACEMENTS | SUMMER INTERNSHIPS

UNIVERSITY PROMOTIONS DURING 2024-2025

ASTON, BATH, BIRMINGHAM, BRADFORD, BRISTOL, BRUNEL, CAMBRIDGE, CARDIFF, COVENTRY, DURHAM, EAST LONDON, EDINBURGH, ESSEX, EXETER, GLASGOW, GREENWICH, HERIOT-WATT, IMPERIAL COLLEGE LONDON, KEELE, KENT, KING'S COLLEGE LONDON, KINGSTON, LANCASTER, LEEDS, LEICESTER, LIVERPOOL JOHN MOORES, LIVERPOOL, LONDON METROPOLITAN, LONDON SOUTHBANK, LOUGHBOROUGH, LSE, MANCHESTER METROPOLITAN, MANCHESTER, MIDDLESEX, NEWCASTLE, NOTTINGHAM TRENT, NOTTINGHAM, OXFORD, QUEEN MARY LONDON, QUEENS UNIVERSITY BELFAST, READING, ROBERT GORDON, SHEFFIELD HALLAM, SHEFFIELD, SOUTHAMPTON, ST ANDREWS, SURREY, SUSSEX, SWANSEA, ULSTER, UNIVERSITY COLLEGE LONDON, WARWICK, WEST OF ENGLAND (UWE)

APPLICATION DEADLINE

Year-round recruitment

FURTHER INFORMATION

www.Top100GraduateEmployers.com

*Register now for the latest news, local promotions, work experience and graduate vacancies at **PwC**.*

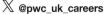

careers.rolls-royce.com

@RollsRoyce_Careers linkedin.com/company/rolls-royce

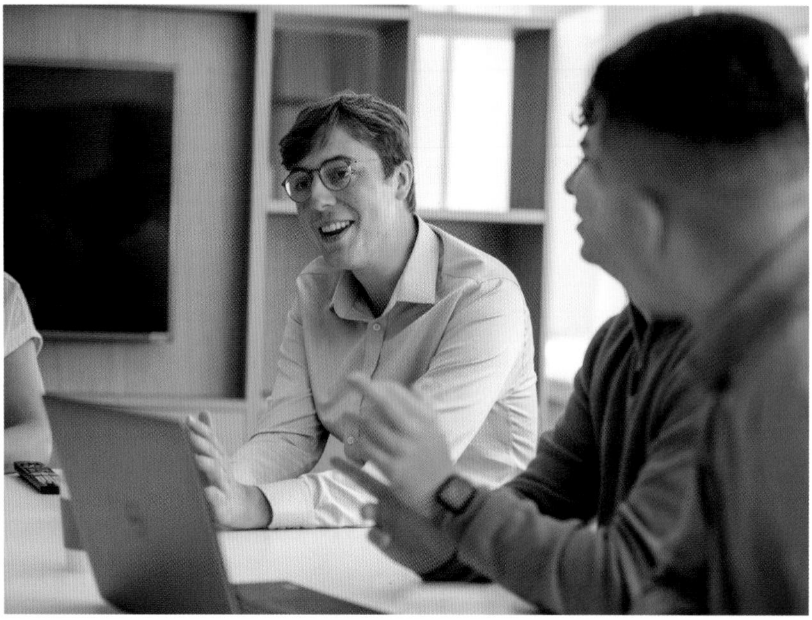

Rolls-Royce has been at the forefront of innovation for more than a hundred years, helping to power, protect and connect the modern world. Through their complex power and propulsion solutions, this iconic business is playing an important role in supporting the energy transition.

When graduates kickstart their career with Rolls-Royce, they're defining the future on their own terms. Each journey with the company starts with a strong but simple belief – everyone is unique and every Rolls-Royce journey is different. Along with the freedom to choose opportunities that will help them develop in the way they want, successful applicants will get the space, skills and support to discover who they can be.

Whether they choose engineering and technology or business and enterprise, the programmes extend across the whole company, offering different experiences to graduates. Learning-focused, programmes concentrate on providing real-world experiences and work on live projects across the different divisions and functions.

The world needs innovation, and Rolls-Royce are focused on shaping the future of cleaner, safer and more sustainable power. They are seeking candidates with a diverse range of talents and different ways of thinking. People who share this vision and will challenge perceptions. That's why the engineering & technology programme is open to all STEM degree subjects and their business programme is open to all subjects.

Rolls-Royce's 12-month internships and 10-week summer internships provide a fantastic insight into life and work at Rolls-Royce. They also offer 6-month internships if needed, as well as direct entry-level positions, so candidates don't have to wait to get started in the career they want. Learn, grow and thrive in an inclusive environment that values each employee as an individual.

GRADUATE VACANCIES IN 2025

- ENGINEERING
- GENERAL MANAGEMENT
- TECHNOLOGY

NUMBER OF VACANCIES

No fixed quota

LOCATIONS OF VACANCIES

STARTING SALARY FOR 2025

£29,000

Plus a £2,000 joining bonus.

WORK EXPERIENCE

DEGREE PLACEMENTS | SUMMER INTERNSHIPS

UNIVERSITY PROMOTIONS DURING 2024-2025

ASTON, BATH, BIRMINGHAM, BRISTOL, CAMBRIDGE, DURHAM, EDINBURGH, GLASGOW, IMPERIAL COLLEGE LONDON, LEICESTER, LOUGHBOROUGH, MANCHESTER, NOTTINGHAM, SHEFFIELD, SOUTHAMPTON, STRATHCLYDE, WARWICK

Please check with your university careers service for full details of Rolls-Royce's local promotions and events.

MINIMUM ENTRY REQUIREMENTS

Relevant degree required for some roles.

APPLICATION DEADLINE

November 2024

FURTHER INFORMATION

www.Top100GraduateEmployers.com

*Register now for the latest news, local promotions, work experience and graduate vacancies at **Rolls-Royce**.*

ROYAL AIR FORCE

recruitment.raf.mod.uk

linkedin.com/company/royal-air-force
@raf_recruitment RAFRecruitment
@rafrecruitment youtube.com/royalairforce

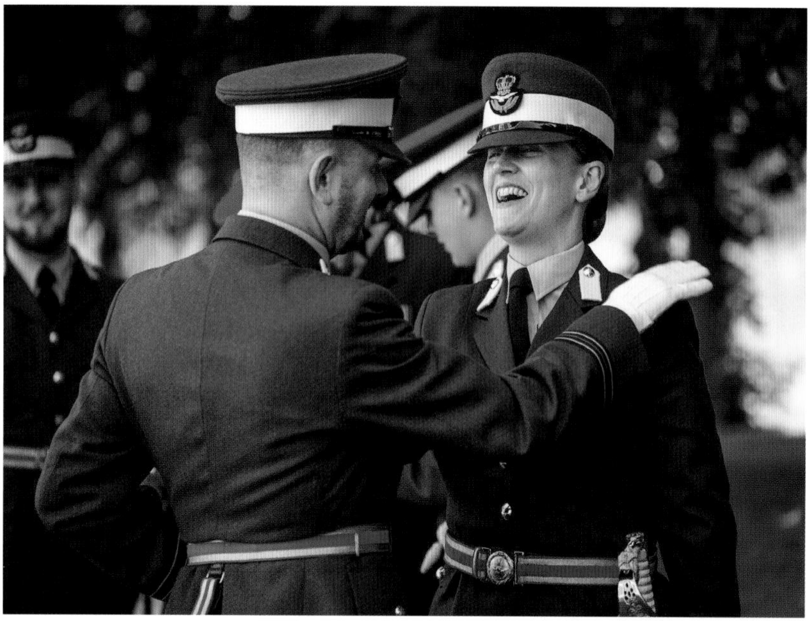

The Royal Air Force (RAF) brings together cutting-edge technology, a wide range of aircraft, and a broad spectrum of capabilities, to provide global air and space power to protect our nation and help it prosper, whilst promoting peace and stability, and acting as a force for good in the world.

To do so, requires a team of people with the right skills and abilities, and with the right mindset and motivation. It is the people's professionalism, dedication and courage that ensures the RAF remains a dynamic air force, able to deliver capability all over the world; be that in support of combat missions or humanitarian aid and disaster relief. Whilst the exploitation of cutting-edge technologies helps meet these challenges; it is essential that the RAF continues to recruit and select high calibre graduates, for officer roles, to lead the RAF of tomorrow.

Graduates joining the RAF, as a commissioned Officer, have been selected because they have demonstrated that they have the potential to be a leader. As an Officer they will be expected to lead and manage RAF personnel, for whom they are responsible, to meet the operational challenges of today and tomorrow. The world-class training received by RAF Officers starts from day one with 6 months training delivered at RAF Cranwell, this is followed by further specialist training based on the area of specialisation chosen.

There are more than twenty different graduate career opportunities, including engineering, aircrew, logistics and personnel roles, as well as medical opportunities for qualified doctors, nurses and dentists. In return, the RAF offers a competitive salary with yearly increases, subsidised food and accommodation, free medical and dental care, opportunities to travel and undertake adventurous training opportunities.

GRADUATE VACANCIES IN 2025
- ENGINEERING
- GENERAL MANAGEMENT
- HUMAN RESOURCES
- LAW
- LOGISTICS
- TECHNOLOGY

NUMBER OF VACANCIES
500+ graduate jobs

LOCATIONS OF VACANCIES

STARTING SALARY FOR 2025
£37,425
after initial officer training (6 months). Plus subsidised living & food charges, free gym membership, paid holiday and a non contributory pension.

UNIVERSITY PROMOTIONS DURING 2024-2025
ABERDEEN, ABERYSTWYTH, BIRMINGHAM, BRIGHTON, BRISTOL, CARDIFF, DERBY, DUNDEE, DURHAM, EDINBURGH, EXETER, GLASGOW, HERIOT-WATT, HUDDERSFIELD, HULL, IMPERIAL COLLEGE LONDON, LANCASTER, LEEDS, LEICESTER, LINCOLN, LIVERPOOL, LOUGHBOROUGH, MANCHESTER, NEWCASTLE, NORTHUMBRIA, NOTTINGHAM, PLYMOUTH, PORTSMOUTH, READING, SHEFFIELD, SOUTHAMPTON, ST ANDREWS, STIRLING, SURREY, SWANSEA, YORK
Please check with your university careers service for full details of the RAF's local promotions and events.

MINIMUM ENTRY REQUIREMENTS
Relevant degree required for some roles.

APPLICATION DEADLINE
Year-round recruitment

FURTHER INFORMATION
www.Top100GraduateEmployers.com
Register now for the latest news, local promotions, work experience and graduate vacancies at the RAF.

ROYAL NAVY

royalnavy.mod.uk/careers

@RoyalNavy RoyalNavyRecruitment

The Royal Navy is, first and foremost, a fighting force. Serving alongside Britain's allies in conflicts around the world, the Royal Navy also vitally protects UK ports, fishing grounds, and merchant ships, helping to combat international smuggling, terrorism, and piracy.

Throughout the course of history, a life at sea has always attracted those with a taste for travel and adventure; but there are plenty of other reasons for graduates and final-year students to consider a challenging and wide-ranging career with the Royal Navy. Graduates will receive a structured route through the ranks, with fast-track, on-the-job training as a constant feature.

Graduates can join the Royal Navy as Officers – the senior leadership and management team in the various professions, which range from engineering, sub-surface, and warfare to medical, the Fleet Air Arm, and logistics. Starting salaries of £31,000, rising to £38,700 in the second year, compare well with those in industry. Those wanting to join the Royal Navy as an Engineer – with Marine, Weapon, or Air Engineer Officer, above or below the water – could work on anything from sensitive electronics to massive gas-turbine engines and nuclear weapons. Increasingly, its 30,000 personnel are involved in humanitarian and relief missions; situations where their skills, discipline, and resourcefulness make a real difference to people's lives. What's more, the Royal Navy can offer a secure, flexible career, with the potential to extend to age 50.

The Royal Navy offers opportunities for early responsibility, career development, sport, recreation, and travel which exceed any in civilian life. With its global reach and responsibilities, the Royal Navy offers plenty of adventure and the chance to see the world, while pursuing one of the most challenging, varied, and fulfilling careers available.

GRADUATE VACANCIES IN 2025

- ENGINEERING
- FINANCE
- GENERAL MANAGEMENT
- HUMAN RESOURCES
- LAW
- LOGISTICS
- MEDIA
- RESEARCH & DEVELOPMENT
- TECHNOLOGY

NUMBER OF VACANCIES

No fixed quota

LOCATIONS OF VACANCIES

Vacancies also available elsewhere in the world.

STARTING SALARY FOR 2025

£31,000

Some roles may receive a joining bonus.

WORK EXPERIENCE

INSIGHT COURSES | DEGREE PLACEMENTS | SUMMER INTERNSHIPS

UNIVERSITY PROMOTIONS DURING 2024-2025

Please check with your university careers service for full details of the Royal Navy's local promotions and events.

MINIMUM ENTRY REQUIREMENTS

Relevant degree required for some roles.

APPLICATION DEADLINE

Year-round recruitment

FURTHER INFORMATION

www.Top100GraduateEmployers.com

Register now for the latest news, local promotions, work experience and graduate vacancies at the ***Royal Navy.***

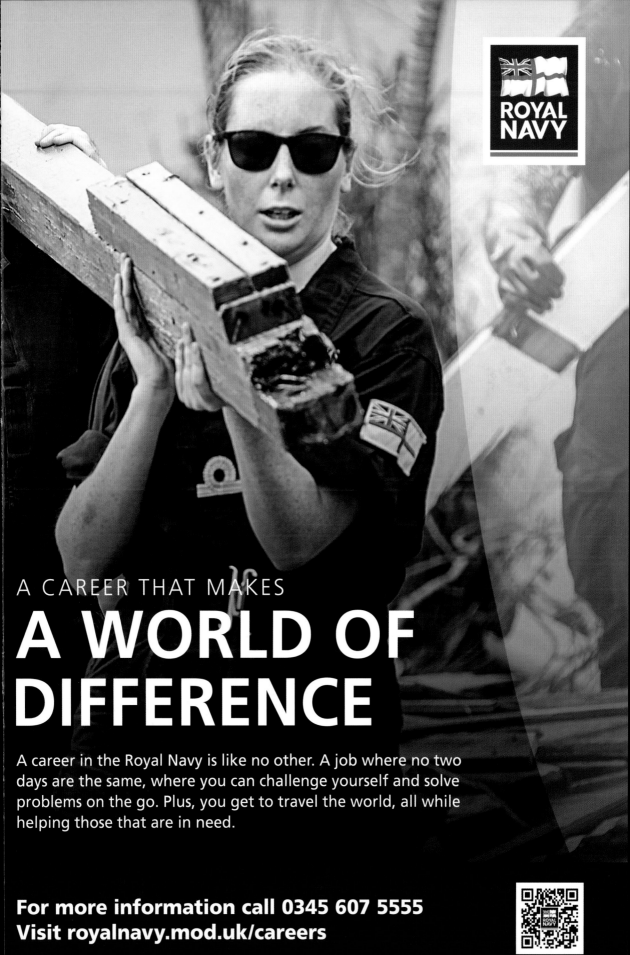

ROYAL
NAVY
A CAREER THAT MAKES
A WORLD OF
DIFFERENCE
A career in the Royal Navy is like no other. A job where no two days are the same, where you can challenge yourself and solve problems on the go. Plus, you get to travel the world, all while helping those that are in need.
For more information call 0345 607 5555
Visit royalnavy.mod.uk/careers

Santander

santander.com/en/careers/uk-careers

Santander is a world-leading banking group. But just like grades or degrees, that doesn't really tell the whole story. Santander is there for customers in the moments that matter – whether that's helping them to resolve a problem or query, or supporting them to achieve their next life goal.

At Santander, their graduate programmes have been designed to bring out the best in participants, providing graduates with training and opportunities to set their potential free. It's not their background or degree that matters (or who they know and how they can blend in), but their unique perspective and drive to succeed. Essentially, what makes each individual unique.

Graduates who join Santander will complete a course that matches their ambitions and interests – and gain a recognised qualification once they complete it. The courses generally span around 18 months with time off for studying built in. With programmes in retail, finance, corporate and commercial banking, risk & compliance, and treasury, every graduate scheme is different, and the skills needed across each one will vary.

Santander also offer various mentorship programmes and access to networks across the bank, with a variety of opportunities to help graduates develop the knowledge, skills and networks needed to launch an exceptional career. Successful participants will take part in a broad range of projects throughout the programme – rotating around different business areas to ensure they make the most of their time with Santander, and discover what truly inspires and drives them forward.

By the end of the graduate programme, participants will have gained the professional experiences needed to help them decide what kind of story they want to write – and what next step to take in their careers.

GRADUATE VACANCIES IN 2025

- FINANCE
- GENERAL MANAGEMENT
- INVESTMENT BANKING
- RETAIL
- TECHNOLOGY

NUMBER OF VACANCIES
75 graduate jobs

LOCATIONS OF VACANCIES

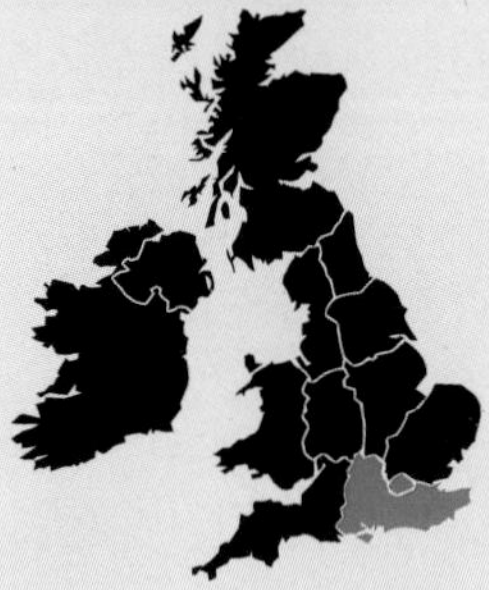

STARTING SALARY FOR 2025
£35,000
Plus a discretionary yearly performance bonus.

WORK EXPERIENCE
SUMMER INTERNSHIPS

UNIVERSITY PROMOTIONS DURING 2024-2025
Please check with your university careers service for full details of Santander's local promotions and events.

MINIMUM ENTRY REQUIREMENTS
112 UCAS points

APPLICATION DEADLINE
Please see website for full details.

FURTHER INFORMATION
www.Top100GraduateEmployers.com
*Register now for the latest news, local promotions, work experience and graduate vacancies at **Santander**.*

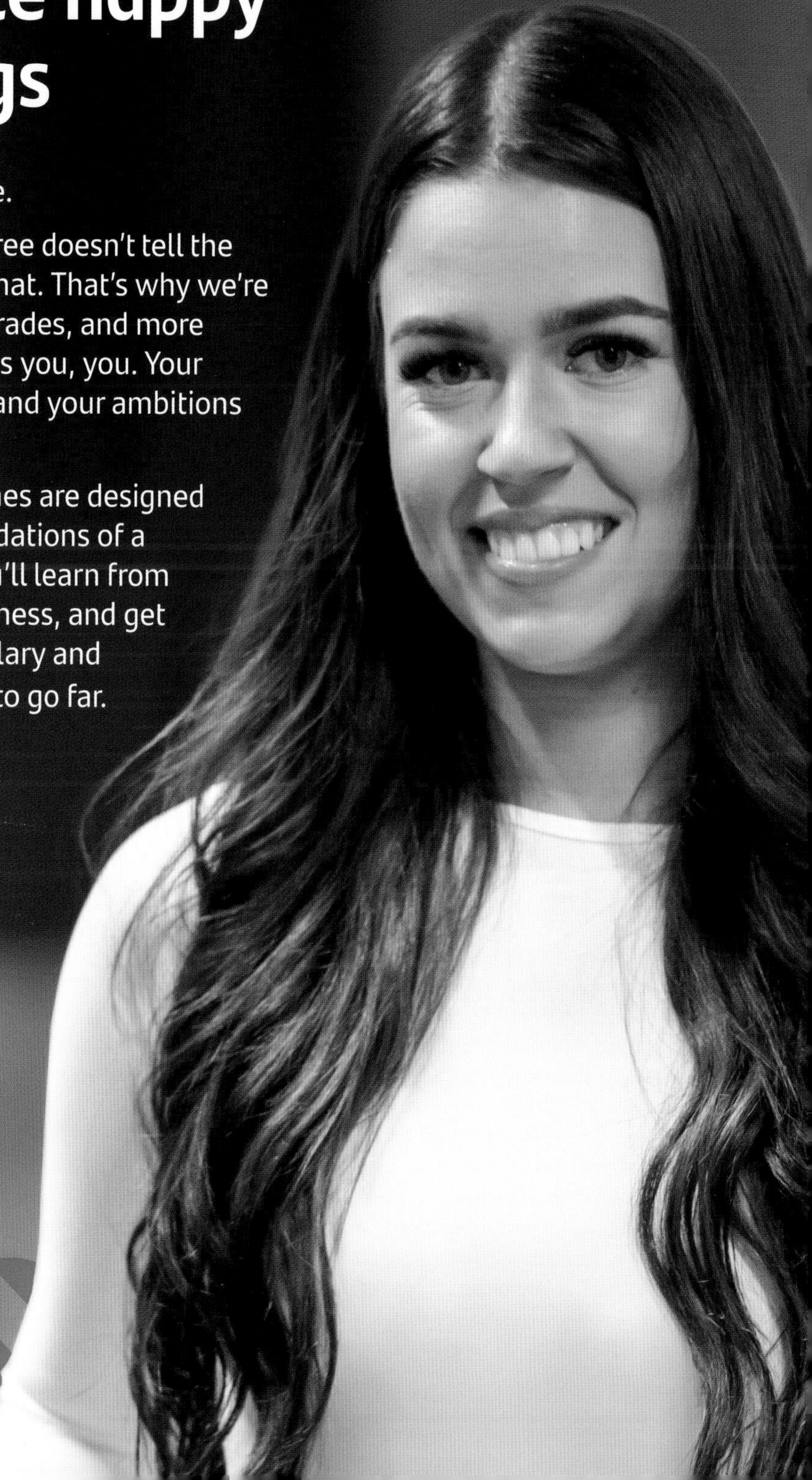

savills

savills.co.uk/apply/current-graduate-vacancies.aspx

@savillsinstagrad

Savills is a world leading property agent, employing over 40,000 people across 700 offices. Their expertise spans the globe and they offer wide-ranging specialist knowledge. Savills take pride in providing the best-in-class advice as they help individuals, businesses and institutions make better property decisions.

Savills' graduate programme offers the chance to gain internationally recognised professional qualifications. The company offers roles within surveying, planning, sustainability, energy, engineering, rural, food & farming and forestry, with half of these vacancies in regional locations. The company has offices in exciting locations around the UK, where fee earners work with varied and prestigious clients. The diversity of Savills' services means there is the flexibility to carve out a fulfilling, self-tailored career path in many locations.

Savills offers up to 150 placement opportunities, each year. Including a one week insight programme for first year students, a one month summer scheme for second year property students, or final year non-property students, and a 12 month year in industry, called the Sandwich Placement, for relevant 3rd year students. Savills passionately believe that their graduates are future leaders, and as such make a huge investment in them.

Savills graduates are given responsibility from day one, in teams who highly value their contribution, allowing them to be involved in some of the world's most high-profile property deals and developments. Graduates are surrounded by expert professionals and experienced team members from whom they learn and seek advice. Individual achievement is rewarded, and Savills look for graduates with entrepreneurial flair. A great work-life balance, structured training and a dynamic working environment are amongst the factors which see Savills as The Times Graduate Recruitment Award's winning employer for Property year-on-year.

GRADUATE VACANCIES IN 2025

ENGINEERING

PROPERTY

NUMBER OF VACANCIES

130+ graduate jobs

LOCATIONS OF VACANCIES

STARTING SALARY FOR 2025

£25,000-£30,000

Plus a sign-on bonus of up to £1,500.

WORK EXPERIENCE

INSIGHT COURSES | DEGREE PLACEMENTS | SUMMER INTERNSHIPS

UNIVERSITY PROMOTIONS DURING 2024-2025

Please check with your university careers service for full details of Savills' local promotions and events.

APPLICATION DEADLINE

16th September - 4th November 2024

FURTHER INFORMATION

www.Top100GraduateEmployers.com

Register now for the latest news, local promotions, work experience and graduate vacancies at ***Savills.***

SLAUGHTER AND MAY/

slaughterandmay.com

trainee.recruit@slaughterandmay.com

@SlaughterandMayCareers

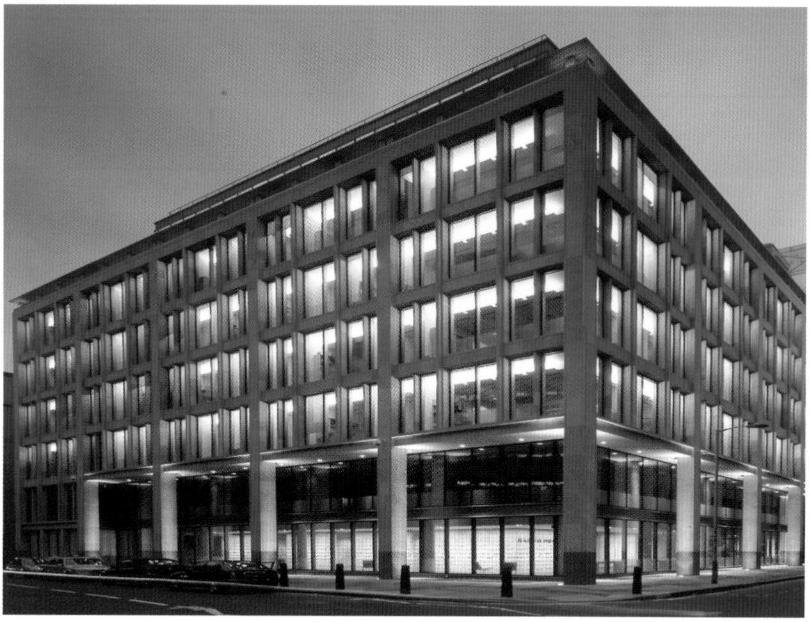

Slaughter and May is one of the most prestigious law firms in the world. The strength of their global practice is reflected both in the multi-jurisdictional nature of their work and their international client base. The firm is a trusted adviser to some of the largest global companies in the world.

There are distinct differences that set Slaughter and May apart from other global law firms. These differences are in relation to their international approach, multi-specialist training, and lack of billable targets.

Slaughter and May work with the very best law firms across the globe to support their clients, handpicked to meet the needs of each matter, to deliver integrated legal advice. Fundamental to their business model is the ability to work in partnership with other law firms – this is how they have built their successful global practice.

Slaughter and May lawyers are all trained to be multi-specialists across a broad range of legal matters. This is hard work, but their lawyers say it makes for a far more fulfilling career. It provides challenge and interest, and also allows their lawyers to develop deeper relationships with clients as they have a better understanding of their businesses. Their lawyers are not set billing targets, and are therefore free to work collaboratively. They share expertise and knowledge in order to concentrate on what matters most – the quality of their work and client service.

Slaughter and May takes great pride in drawing strength from diversity and believes that an inclusive workplace drives collaboration and enhances business performance. They are looking to employ the brightest minds regardless of what or where they studied. They offer open days and work experience schemes to enable applicants to gain an insight into life as a commercial lawyer.

GRADUATE VACANCIES IN 2025

LAW

NUMBER OF VACANCIES

95 graduate jobs

For training contracts starting in 2027.

LOCATIONS OF VACANCIES

STARTING SALARY FOR 2025

£56,000

WORK EXPERIENCE

INSIGHT COURSES | SUMMER INTERNSHIPS

UNIVERSITY PROMOTIONS DURING 2024-2025

Please check with your university careers service for full details of Slaughter and May's local promotions and events.

MINIMUM ENTRY REQUIREMENTS

2.1 Degree

APPLICATION DEADLINE

Please see website for full details.

FURTHER INFORMATION

www.Top100GraduateEmployers.com

*Register now for the latest news, local promotions, work experience and graduate vacancies at **Slaughter and May**.*

teachfirst.org.uk/training-programme

Teach First

TeachFirst | recruitment@teachfirst.org.uk
@TeachFirst | linkedin.com/company/teach-first
@TeachFirstUK | youtube.com/TeachFirstYT

Right now, there are children in this country who won't get the education they deserve. It's not okay and it's not fair. Since 2003, Teach First have been improving the life chances for children living in disadvantaged communities by training brilliant teachers to work in the schools that need them the most.

Graduates have many career options ahead of them, but few are more meaningful than teaching. For 20 years, Teach First has been fighting to give every child the chance to fulfil their potential. It begins with getting great teachers into the schools that need them the most.

Teach First's Training Programme is the largest teacher training and leadership programme in the UK. It offers graduates a competitive salary while they train and opens the door to a world of career possibilities. Over two years, they'll qualify as teachers, gain a fully-funded qualification, receive professional coaching worth over £10k, and develop an array of transferable leadership skills.

From their first day in the classroom, trainees make an instant impact on the lives of young people, in a role where no two days are the same. With support from Teach First, trainees are seven times more likely to progress into leadership roles early in their careers. The charity has an influential network of 17,750+ teachers and leaders, both inside and outside the classroom, as well as links to a range of organisations, many of which offer trainees extra opportunities to hone their leadership skills through coaching and summer projects. From day one trainees will be in the classroom, starting with 80% of a fully qualified teacher's timetable (60% for primary and early years).

The challenge is real, but so is the chance to create lasting change. This is the most important generation of teachers and leaders, joining Teach First to fight for a fairer future. Visit the Teach First website to find out more and apply now.

GRADUATE VACANCIES IN 2025
TEACHING

NUMBER OF VACANCIES
1,750 graduate jobs

LOCATIONS OF VACANCIES

STARTING SALARY FOR 2025
£Competitive

WORK EXPERIENCE
INSIGHT COURSES

UNIVERSITY PROMOTIONS DURING 2024-2025
ABERDEEN, ABERYSTWYTH, ASTON, BANGOR, BATH, BELFAST, BIRMINGHAM, BRADFORD, BRISTOL, CAMBRIDGE, CARDIFF, CITY, DURHAM, EDINBURGH, ESSEX, EXETER, GLASGOW, HERIOT-WATT, HULL, IMPERIAL COLLEGE LONDON, KEELE, KING'S COLLEGE LONDON, KENT, LANCASTER, LEEDS, LEICESTER, LIVERPOOL, LONDON SCHOOL OF ECONOMICS, LOUGHBOROUGH, MANCHESTER, NEWCASTLE, NORTHUMBRIA, NOTTINGHAM, NOTTINGHAM TRENT, OXFORD, OXFORD BROOKES, PLYMOUTH, QUEEN MARY LONDON, READING, ROYAL HOLLOWAY, SCHOOL OF AFRICAN STUDIES, SHEFFIELD, SOUTHAMPTON, ST ANDREWS, SURREY, SUSSEX, SWANSEA, UEA, UNIVERSITY COLLEGE LONDON, WARWICK, YORK

MINIMUM ENTRY REQUIREMENTS
2.1 Degree
However, all applications are assessed on a case-by-case basis.

APPLICATION DEADLINE
Year-round recruitment

FURTHER INFORMATION
www.Top100GraduateEmployers.com
Register now for the latest news, local promotions, work experience and graduate vacancies at ***Teach First.***

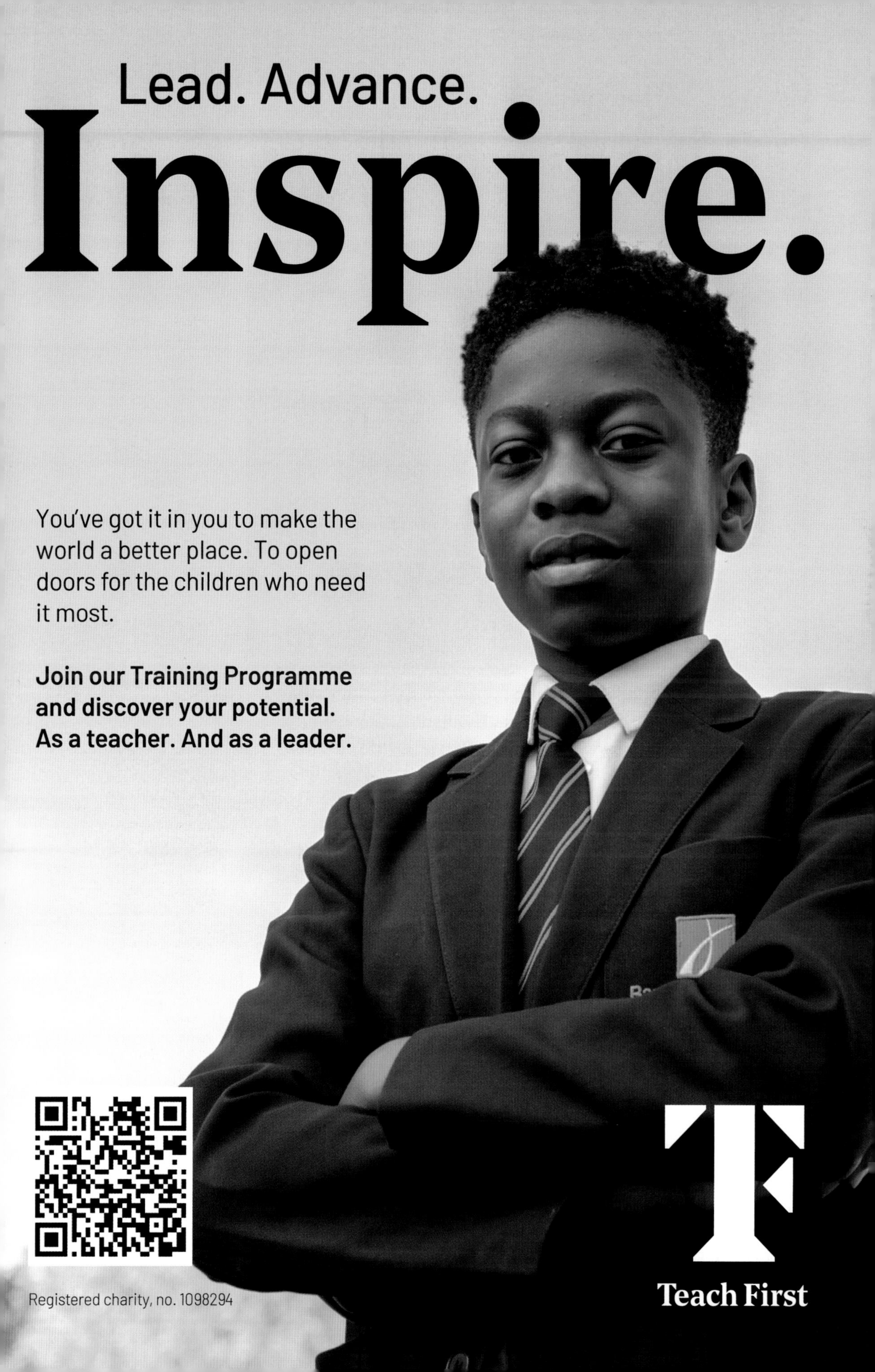
Lead. Advance.
Inspire.
You've got it in you to make the world a better place. To open doors for the children who need it most.
Join our Training Programme and discover your potential. As a teacher. And as a leader.
Registered charity, no. 1098294
Teach First

Transport for London

tfl.gov.uk/corporate/careers/graduates

transportforlondon | earlycareerscampaigns@tfl.gov.uk
@tfl | linkedin.com/company/transport-for-london
@transportforlondon | youtube.com/transportforlondon

Transport for London (TfL) are responsible for the day-to-day operation of London's public transport network and manage London's main roads. They are committed to achieving the Mayor's goal of making London carbon neutral by 2030 and supporting a green recovery to become a world-leading smart city.

TfL offers a diverse range of opportunities including graduate schemes, summer placements and industry internships. Opportunities vary from engineering, project management, real estate, operations, technology, finance and many other areas. Each programme provides comprehensive training and development opportunities to help build a successful career. Individuals will gain hands-on experience, work on impactful projects, and contribute to the smooth functioning of London's transport network. Roles are based across London with hybrid working depending on the placement.

The graduate development programme consists of up to 6 structured placement rotations which vary from 3 to 6 months, giving graduates the opportunity to work on several projects. Technical and professional development is supported through a wide range of on-the-job practical experiences including a combination of classroom-led and online training courses, mentoring and structured networking opportunities with scheme alumni. Some programmes will result in industry recognised qualifications such as Institution of Engineering and Technology (IET), Institution of Civil Engineers (ICE) and others.

One-to-one support is provided through a placement manager, responsible for day-to-day management and support; a scheme sponsor, a senior manager who acts as a technical and professional adviser; and a development adviser, who will support professional development through career coaching and career progression at TfL.

GRADUATE VACANCIES IN 2025

- ENGINEERING
- FINANCE
- GENERAL MANAGEMENT
- HUMAN RESOURCES
- MEDIA
- PROPERTY
- PURCHASING
- TECHNOLOGY

NUMBER OF VACANCIES

50+ graduate jobs

LOCATIONS OF VACANCIES

STARTING SALARY FOR 2025

£29,500+

2025 salary to be confirmed.

WORK EXPERIENCE

INSIGHT COURSES | SUMMER INTERNSHIPS

UNIVERSITY PROMOTIONS DURING 2024-2025

BRUNEL, CITY, ESSEX, IMPERIAL COLLEGE LONDON, LSE, QUEEN MARY LONDON, UEA, UNIVERSITY COLLEGE LONDON

Please check with your university careers service for full details of TfL's local promotions and events.

MINIMUM ENTRY REQUIREMENTS

2.2 Degree

Relevant degree required for some roles.

APPLICATION DEADLINE

November - December 2024

FURTHER INFORMATION

www.Top100GraduateEmployers.com

Register now for the latest news, local promotions, work experience and graduate vacancies at TfL.

Unlocked

unlockedgrads.org.uk

UnlockedGrads | hello@unlockedgrads.org.uk
@UnlockedGrads | linkedin.com/school/unlocked-graduates
@UnlockedGrads | youtube.com/unlockedgraduates

Unlocked Graduates recruits, trains, and challenges outstanding individuals to lead prisoner rehabilitation with the aim of creating high-performing leaders who will break the cycles of reoffending in prisons and throughout society. The programme puts brilliant graduates at the heart of prison reform.

Nearly half of all adult prisoners reoffend within one year of leaving prison, creating more victims, untold damage, and a cost of over £18 billion. The problems facing prisons are some of the most complex in society. That is the challenge at the heart of the Unlocked Graduates leadership development programme.

Unlocked looks for ambitious graduates who are passionate about shaping the system for the better. It is a chance to join a graduate scheme that sees participants have real impact, on the frontline through their work with prisoners on the landings and across the wider system through innovative research projects.

The award-winning programme combines academic study with real world experience providing the platform to trial and assess solutions within prisons. They offer a fully funded master's degree, a highly competitive salary, specialised mentoring, and work placement opportunities with key employers. And, in their second year, graduates get to write and present a policy paper to the Government.

After they finish the programme, many graduates choose to stay within the justice system or go on to make a difference in a variety of prestigious careers. Alumni have attended international conferences in Lisbon and Madrid, shared best practice with prisons in the US and Norway, and won awards such as the Prime Minister's award. But no matter where their career takes them, Unlocked continues to support this growing network of change-makers.

GRADUATE VACANCIES IN 2025
PRISON OFFICER

NUMBER OF VACANCIES
143 graduate jobs

LOCATIONS OF VACANCIES

STARTING SALARY FOR 2025
Up to £40,000

UNIVERSITY PROMOTIONS DURING 2024-2025
ABERDEEN, ASTON, BATH, BELFAST, BIRMINGHAM, BIRMINGHAM CITY, BRISTOL, CAMBRIDGE, CARDIFF, DE MONTFORT UNVERSITY, DURHAM, EDINBURGH, EDINBURGH NAPIER, EXETER, GLASGOW, HERIOT-WATT, IMPERIAL COLLEGE LONDON, KING'S COLLEGE LONDON, LANCASTER, LEEDS, LIVERPOOL, LOUGHBOROUGH, LSE, MANCHESTER, MANCHESTER METROPOLITAN, NEWCASTLE, NOTTINGHAM, OXFORD, QUEEN'S UNIVERSITY, READING, ROBERT GORDON, SHEFFIELD, SOUTHAMPTON, ST ANDREWS, STRATHCLYDE, ULSTER, UNIVERSITY COLLEGE LONDON, WARWICK, YORK

MINIMUM ENTRY REQUIREMENTS
2.1 Degree

APPLICATION DEADLINE
February 2025

FURTHER INFORMATION
www.Top100GraduateEmployers.com
*Register now for the latest news, local promotions, work experience and graduate vacancies at **Unlocked**.*

WHITE & CASE

White & Case is a global law firm of more than 2,500 lawyers worldwide. They've built an unrivalled network of 44 offices in 30 countries. That investment is the foundation for their client work in over 200 countries today. White & Case work with clients that are multinational organisations with complex needs.

White & Case trainees will work on fast-paced, cutting-edge cross-border projects from the outset of their career. As such, White & Case is looking to recruit ambitious trainees who have a desire to gain hands-on practical experience from day one and a willingness to take charge of their own career. They value globally minded citizens of the world who are eager to work across borders and cultures, and who are intrigued by solving problems within multiple legal systems. The White & Case training contract consists of four six-month seats, one in finance, one in a contentious practice area, and one of which is guaranteed to be spent in one of their overseas offices.

They offer vacation scheme placements over the winter, spring, and summer, open days, and two-day insight schemes. These provide a great way to experience first-hand what life is like as a White & Case trainee as well as gain useful insight into the firm and the training they offer.

The firm's virtual learning programme offers the opportunity to gain insight into life as a White & Case trainee and experience the realities of cross-border law. There is no cost to access the platform, it is self-paced to fit around users' schedules, and no application form or legal knowledge is required. Students will gain insight into the fast-paced, cutting-edge projects their lawyers and trainees work on, and gain valuable skills by undertaking true-to-life legal tasks. Participation in the learning platform will be recognised on their application forms.

GRADUATE VACANCIES IN 2025

LAW

NUMBER OF VACANCIES

50 graduate jobs

For training contracts starting in 2027.

LOCATIONS OF VACANCIES

STARTING SALARY FOR 2025

£56,000

WORK EXPERIENCE

INSIGHT COURSES | SUMMER INTERNSHIPS

UNIVERSITY PROMOTIONS DURING 2024-2025

Please check with your university careers service for full details of White & Case's local promotions and events.

MINIMUM ENTRY REQUIREMENTS

2.1 Degree

APPLICATION DEADLINE

Please see website for full details.

FURTHER INFORMATION

www.Top100GraduateEmployers.com

Register now for the latest news, local promotions, work experience and graduate vacancies at ***White & Case.***

wsp.com/graduates-uk

ecpteam@wsp.com

@WSP_UK WSPUK

@wspuk linkedin.com/company/wsp-in-the-uk

WSP is a world-leading multi-disciplinary professional services consulting firm which provides engineering, planning, design and strategic advisory services across the built and natural environments. They have over 9,500 technical specialists in the UK, and over 67,000 staff globally.

Students and graduates can apply to join WSP's graduate programme in the following sectors: transportation and infrastructure, property and buildings, earth and environment, power, energy, water resources, planning and industry sectors, as well as a strategic advisory. They are open to applicants from all engineering, science, digital, data, STEM, economics, business and finance backgrounds. New graduates will be based in one of WSP's 34 regional offices in the UK.

Graduates working towards chartered status are financially supported and provided with a professionally registered mentor for guidance. All graduates are set up to succeed and receive support to enable them to progress in their career.

Placement opportunities are available with 8-12 week paid internships from June to August, and 12 month industrial placements beginning in August or September. Students will work on a range of projects and obtain real industry experience during their placement. Upon successful completion, students may go on to be sponsored via the scholarship programme and return to WSP upon graduation.

The WSP two-year graduate development programme is a combination of business, technical and personal skills training opportunities, supporting graduates to excel early in their career. Graduates work on a diverse set of assignments, enabling them to gain a better understanding of their role on projects. As well as allowing them to engage in initiatives that shape the future and create a lasting impact on communities and the planet.

GRADUATE VACANCIES IN 2025

CONSULTING
ENGINEERING
FINANCE
PROPERTY

NUMBER OF VACANCIES

180+ graduate jobs

LOCATIONS OF VACANCIES

STARTING SALARY FOR 2025

£27,500+

WORK EXPERIENCE

DEGREE PLACEMENTS | SUMMER INTERNSHIPS

UNIVERSITY PROMOTIONS DURING 2024-2025

BATH, BIRMINGHAM, BRISTOL, CAMBRIDGE, CARDIFF, CENTRAL LANCASHIRE, DURHAM, EDINBURGH NAPIER, EXETER, GLASGOW, GLASGOW CALEDONIAN, IMPERIAL COLLEGE LONDON, LEEDS, LIVERPOOL, LOUGHBOROUGH, MANCHESTER, NEWCASTLE, NORTHUMBRIA, NOTTINGHAM, PORTSMOUTH, QUEEN'S UNIVERSITY BELFAST, SHEFFIELD, SOUTHAMPTON, SURREY, ULSTER, UNIVERSITY COLLEGE LONDON

Please check with your university careers service for full details of WSP's local promotions and events.

MINIMUM ENTRY REQUIREMENTS

2.2 Degree

APPLICATION DEADLINE

25th November 2024

Applications will reopen two days after, until all roles are filled. Subject to change.

FURTHER INFORMATION

www.Top100GraduateEmployers.com

*Register now for the latest news, local promotions, work experience and graduate vacancies at **WSP**.*

Useful Information

EMPLOYER	GRADUATE RECRUITMENT WEBSITE
A&O SHEARMAN	earlycareersuk.aoshearman.com
AECOM	aecom.com/uk-ireland-graduate-careers
AIRBUS	airbus.com/en/careers/graduates
ALDI	aldirecruitment.co.uk/area-manager-programme
AMAZON	amazon.jobs
AON	aon.com/careers/uk
ARUP	careers.arup.com/earlycareers
ASTRAZENECA	careers.astrazeneca.com/early-talent
ATKINSRÉALIS	careers.atkinsrealis.com/uk-early-careers
BAE SYSTEMS	baesystems.com/graduates
BANK OF AMERICA	campus.bankofamerica.com
BARCLAYS	search.jobs.barclays
BBC	bbc.co.uk/earlycareers
BCG	careers.bcg.com
BDO	careers.bdo.co.uk
BLACKROCK	careers.blackrock.com/early-careers
BLOOMBERG	bloomberg.com/company/what-we-do
BRITISH AIRWAYS	careers.ba.com/graduates-bps-and-interns
CAPGEMINI	capgemini.com/gb-en/careers/career-paths
CIVIL SERVICE	faststream.gov.uk
CLYDE & CO	careers.clydeco.com/en/early-careers
DELOITTE	deloitte.co.uk/careers
DEUTSCHE BANK	careers.db.com/students-graduates
DIAGEO	diageo.com/en/careers/early-careers
DLA PIPER	earlycareers.dlapiper.com/uk
DYSON	careers.dyson.com/early-careers
ENTERPRISE MOBILITY	careers.enterprise.co.uk
EY	ey.com/uk/students
FORVIS MAZARS	jobs.mazars.co.uk/jobs/early-careers
FRESHFIELDS	freshfields.com/earlycareers
GCHQ	gchq-careers.co.uk/our-careers.html
GOOGLE	google.com/students
GRANT THORNTON	trainees.grantthornton.co.uk
GSK	gsk.com/en-gb/careers/early-talent
HOGAN LOVELLS	graduates.hoganlovells.com

EMPLOYER	GRADUATE RECRUITMENT WEBSITE
HSBC	hsbc.com/earlycareers
IBM	ibm.biz/graduate
ITV	careers.itv.com/teams/early-careers
J.P. MORGAN	jpmorganchase.com/careers
KPMG	kpmgcareers.co.uk
L'ORÉAL	careers.loreal.com/en_US/content/UK
LATHAM & WATKINS	lwcareers.com/en/beginning-your-legal-career
LIDL	lidlgraduatecareers.co.uk
LINKLATERS	careers.linklaters.com
LLOYDS BANKING GROUP	lloydsbankinggrouptalent.com
M&S	jobs.marksandspencer.com/early-careers
MI5 - THE SECURITY SERVICE	mi5.gov.uk/careers
MICROSOFT	careers.microsoft.com/students
MOTT MACDONALD	mottmac.com/careers/uk-and-ireland-early-careers
NATWEST GROUP	jobs.natwestgroup.com
NESTLÉ	nestle.co.uk/nestle-academy
NEWTON	newtoneurope.com/careers/graduates
NHS	graduates.nhs.uk
P&G	pgcareers.com
PENGUIN	penguinrandomhousecareers.co.uk
PFIZER	pfizer.co.uk/careers
POLICE NOW	policenow.org.uk
PWC	pwc.co.uk/careers
ROLLS-ROYCE	careers.rolls-royce.com
ROYAL AIR FORCE	recruitment.raf.mod.uk
ROYAL NAVY	royalnavy.mod.uk/careers
SANTANDER	santander.com/en/careers/uk-careers
SAVILLS	savills.co.uk/apply/current-graduate-vacancies.aspx
SECRET INTELLIGENCE SERVICE (MI6)	sis.gov.uk/explore-careers.html
SLAUGHTER AND MAY	slaughterandmay.com
TEACH FIRST	teachfirst.org.uk/training-programme
TRANSPORT FOR LONDON	tfl.gov.uk/corporate/careers/graduates
UNLOCKED	unlockedgrads.org.uk
WHITE & CASE	whitecasetrainee.com
WSP	wsp.com/graduates-uk